SPACE ACES!

COMIC BOOK HEROES FROM THE FORTIES AND FIFTIES!

A DENIS GIFFORD COLLECTION

GREEN WOOD

A GREEN WOOD BOOK
COPYRIGHT © 1991 THE GREEN WOOD PUBLISHING COMPANY LTD

COPYRIGHT © 1992 TEXT AND COMPILATION DENIS GIFFORD

COPYRIGHT © COMICS: VARIOUS PUBLISHING COMPANIES AS LISTED.

ISBN 1 872532 89 6

PHOTOGRAPHY BY DEREK SMITH AND JAY TAUBEN

DESIGN BY TITAN STUDIO

TYPESET IN GREAT BRITAIN BY TITAN STUDIO

PRINTED AND BOUND IN HONG KONG

THE GREEN WOOD PUBLISHING COMPANY LTD
6/7 WARREN MEWS
LONDON W1P 5DJ

CONTENTS

YOUR PASSPORT TO THE PLANETS!

'Ten centuries from today' – today was August 1946 – 'man has conquered the forces confining him to Earth. Captain Climax, ambassador of good will, leaves Earth to unite the Universe in peace.' The Captain's first planet-of-call is Mercury. Speaking in the Inter-Solar Language, he introduces himself to a passing Mercurian. 'Can you direct me to the Palace of Karka the Ruler?' he queries. 'Accompany me, stranger,' is the reply from a black-clad chap who needs no transparent space helmet, 'I am also going there.' In conversation Climax learns that the people of Mercury appear to be happy, but in fact they are ruled by the iron hand of Karka the Cruel, their dictator. 'Inside Karka's huge palace', states a caption (which saved the artist from having to draw same), Climax explains his mission, to enrol Mercury in the League of the United Universe. Karka seems willing, but no sooner has Climax left the scene than Karka is musing, in italics, *'He must never leave Mercury alive – he will die tomorrow!'*

Tomorrow took some time to come, a whole month, in fact, when *The Climax* number seven was due to hit the bookstalls. This six-pictures-an-episode serial, one single page in a monthly pocket-sized magazine for boys, was too brief to catch abiding interest – especially as *The Climax* collapsed after one more issue! Ronald Flatteau, the publisher, was a dealer in foreign stamps working out of 30 City Road, London EC1. Like many an underfunded individual, he was having a go at being a publisher for the juvenile market in those post-war days of paper controls and Austerity (with a capital 'A'). The artist, aged nineteen and still a Clerk Pay-Accounts in the RAF, was having a bash at his first science-fiction strip, inspired by the title of Flatteau's magazine. He was thrilled to discover that Flatteau had made Captain Climax the two-colour cover star in the typical red-and-blue of the period – but less so when he spotted the clumsy redrawing of his hero by an unnamed amateur hand. And I'm still pretty vexed! Yes, that young comic artist was me!

I had bought the first number of *The Climax* on one of my on-leave expeditions by bicycle to a scruffy little second-hand shop in Catford, South London, called 'The Bookeries'. This tottering junkpile was run, or more likely limped, by an equally tottering old gent called Mr Oliver. He sat in the back behind a flapdown counter, coughing himself to death over a Woodbine as he crouched around

a battered Valor oilstove to keep himself warm. On his head was a purple beret, on his hands fingerless gloves which would be flattered to be called mittens. Surrounding him were the piles of old comics, *Knockouts, Radio Funs, Film Funs*, all of them half-price. This averaged out at three-ha'pence each. Such was the high cost of comic collecting back in the mid-Forties!

Ever eager to expand my freelance cartooning activities, I hastily raced home to Sydenham and spent at least an hour of my 'forty-eight' working out and posting in the first page of Captain Climax. The confidence of youth was swiftly rewarded by Mr Flatteau, who offered me a pound a page to draw one episode a month for his new mag. It doesn't sound much today, but at 240 pence a pound, it would buy quite a pile of old comics from Mr Oliver's shop!

Science fiction had been a special interest of mine ever since Mum took me to see the H.G. Wells movie, *Things to Come*, back in 1936. The wonderful music used during a montage of a new world being built haunted me for years, and was often played on the radio in those days. I tried to make some of the futuristic tanks out of paper and fishglue – Dad had told me the film used models – and the visual image of the great aeroplanes looming out of the clouds is marked in my memory-banks to this day. There were some sci-fi strips of a sort in the comics of my childhood: 'Rob the Rover' in the twopenny *Puck* was always roaring round the world, and under the sea, in his streamlined super-ship. But it was the Fifties before sci-fi really got started, first with George Pal's astounding semi-documentary, *Destination Moon*, pipped at the cinematic post by Robert L. Lippert's B-Movie variation, *Rocketship XM*. Where the cinema led, comics followed.

My own entry into the sci-fi world really happened in 1952. I was drawing 'Flip and Flop' and other comic characters for Mick Anglo's comic-books when I conceived my great idea. Within a month I had compiled and launched *Space Patrol Official Handbook*, from the Space Patrol Headquarters, 16 Sydenham Park, SE26! 'Your Passport to the Planets', as I advertised it, contained 'Everything you want to know about the Life on Other Planets, Space Suits, Spacecraft Recognition, Insignia, Interplanetary Languages – plus Space Patrol Membership Certificate! Secret Codes of the Spaceways!

Interplanetary Passport! Gazetteer of the Galaxy! Real Photographs of Spaceships! (pinched from space films, of course) and the Space Man's Code of Honour!' Also a 'Free Jet-ex Jet-propelled Rocket Ship in Easy Competition! – It Flies!' All this and more in one twenty-page blue-covered booklet for a one-and-sixpenny Postal Order! A word of warning – don't send a 1s 6d PO to the SPHQ, will you? I sold out and moved! Anyway, as there are only two known copies left, the *Handbook* would now cost a little more than seven and a half pence!

Mick Anglo, who published my adverts in his L. Miller comic-books, invited me to try my hand at drawing sci-fi strips for his new all-British title, *Space Comics,* as a support to his own Captain Valiant. Always willing to have a go, especially as my rates

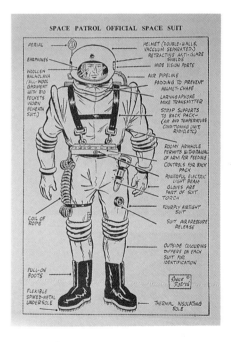

had risen from £1 a page to £1.17s 6d (Mick kept the odd half-a-crown to pay himself for the lettering!), I created 'Speedsmith – Trouble Shooter'. He began in *Space Comics* No. 56 (October 1953) and was followed by 'Jet Black – Rocket Man' in Mick's companion comic-book, *Space Commando* No. 56 (January 1954).

I also wrote and drew a third series, 'Now It Can Be Told', which began with 'Eye of a Spy' in *Space Comics* No. 60 (November 1953) and added the odd-ball 'Planet Facts' page from No. 67 (January 1954). This dealt with such astounding stuff as the Clugadug of Mercury: 'Has six eyes, six legs and a hand on its tail – yet no teeth!' Apparently it trapped birds in its mouth by use of a twig. When the bird flew down to pick up the twig for a nest, the Clugadug promptly swallowed bird and twig!

After seventeen six-pagers of Speedsmith, ten of 'Now It Can Be Told', five of Jet Black, thirty pages of 'Planet Facts' and one set of 'Solo Starr – Human Rocket', I turned it in. Even sci-fi purveyors who are sci-fi buffs can draw enough of a goodish thing. However, a taste for space never deserted me, and I later returned to the sci-fi theme in a strip for *Chips*. Slightly aside from my earlier work, it was entitled 'Sammy Sprockett and his Pocket Rocket!'

Well, so much for my own nostalgia. Now it's over to you, the hopefully grown-up readers of those sixpenny comic-books of the Forties and Fifties. Here's a treasury of yesteryear for you – the tomorrow that might have been!

SPACE CONQUERORS

by William McCail
***Thrill Comics* (1940) *Picture Epics* (1952)**
Gerald G. Swan Ltd (London)

The preamble began: 'A story of two Earthmen who dared space to find a marvellous but terrifying underworld inside the Moon. Of a battle of Martian invaders, and a gangster's bid for world power using the vast knowledge of a Martian, Spikey. A thrilling fight with a Venusian spaceship. Finally, a last journey across fifty million miles of space to the red planet, Mars.' Thus the reissue of this Forties strip in the Fifties, as No. 3 of *Picture Epics*. The original serial had started much more simply and matter-of-factly: 'We ought to arrive on the Moon at dawn!' This was episode one of 'Voyage to the Moon' (Adventures of Professor Newton and Buck Preston) in *Thrill Comics* No. 1, published April 1940. Landing on Luna was simple: 'I'm switching on the retarders!' said the Prof. 'The rocket has arrived safely and the Prof's air test says OK!' So much for science. The Moon is, of course, inhabited. First, the footprint of a giant bird, then – 'Careful, boss!' – monsters in a cave, and finally hippo-faced hairies grab them and chain them in an underground cell – in links of solid gold! A moonquake, a sudden flood, and they are free, a fortune in gold on each wrist! Wonders ahead included Moonmen, robots, giant burrowing moles, flying wings, the Grand Lunarian and Spikey the invading Astacus from Mars, a lobsterish crustacean whom they bring back to Earth.

From *Thrill Comics* No. 4 this serial was retitled 'Return of the Rocket'. Billy McCail, a former stalwart of D.C. Thomson's boys' papers, dismissed for politicking, now became a freelance stalwart of Gerald G. Swan's American-style comic-books, where his adventure strips, slapdash but well plotted, became very popular with young readers. The *Picture Epics* edition was edited, partly redrawn, and given a dramatic cover by Billy's brother, John McCail.

SPACE CONQUERORS

1/-

PICTURE EPICS No. 3

52 PICTURE PAGES OF ASTOUNDING SPACE ADVENTURE

CRASH CAREW:
DAREDEVIL OF THE STRATOSPHERE

by Nat Brand
Comic Adventures **(1942)**
A. Soloway Ltd (London)

'Speeding through the stratosphere, Crash Carew and Billy, his assistant, become alarmed as ice begins to form over their planet-rocket.' As with all early sci-fi stories, the adventures of Crash Carew simply began, simply stated, in a most matter-of-fact way. By the end of page one, Crash and Billy are into their protective crash-suits and their ship, 'The Marlin', is nosediving into the Ice Planet. Flip over to the back page of *Comic Adventures* (Volume 2, No. 3), and there are the evil ice-batmen swooping down, tying the two to giant icicles, and leaving them to their frozen doom. Billy, breaking into a broad grin, switches on the heater of his crash-suit and soon they are zooming on their way to more adventures in No. 4. This time five whole pages await them, filled with monster ramphoryns, reptilian brachycans and worse. As with all Crash's adventures, published approximately quarterly, this one ends neatly: 'I think we've seen enough of this planet of reptiles, Billy! Let's push off to pastures new!'

Nat Brand, an untraced artist believed to be Scottish, was a pioneer of American-style strip heroes, creating a Tarzan type in 'Halcon, Lord of the Crater Land', 'Dandy McQueen, Dude of the Royal Mounted', and 'Bentley Price, Private Detective', all for the Soloway group of comic-books. His exciting and stylish artwork was easily the best of the period, and his plotting was both derivative and inspired in its interpretation. As his hero Crash Carew later remarked, 'Am I seeing things, or can it possibly be?'

[Continued on next four pages

ARGO UNDER THE OCEAN

by Nat Brand
All Star Comic **(1942)**
A. Soloway Ltd (London)

Astrange fish bearing a golden tablet is caught and presented to a well-known museum. The tablet is a map of the North Pole and bears the legend, 'Prisoner in Undersea City of Tremuda – SOS.' One man – Argo – a daring adventurer and famous inventor, determines to put his undersea inventions to the supreme test, and sets forth. On skis he trudges through bitter storms, eluding hungry polar bears, encountering wolves, evading musk-oxen with his home-made landslides. Finally he sights the Great Sea. He dons his rubberised electrically-heated suit and, aided by electrical propulsion, cleaves his way through the ocean depths. Attacked by spear-fish and a shoal of barracudas – 'tigers of the sea' – he fires his ray-gun at a monster crawfish and saves the life of a swimming boy. A master of languages, Argo soon makes himself understood by the lad and his guardian, thanks to the application of a microphone to his cellopex face-covering. The couple lead Argo to the undersea city of Tremuda, 'with its severe architecture and myriad current vanes'. The boy takes Argo to Regent Svang, his uncle, who has Argo arrested and confined with Hans, the earthling who inscribed the golden tablet. Hans warns Argo: 'Svang is a positive dictator with one fanatical idea – to construct a mighty war machine under the sea and rise to conquer Earth!' Here ends chapter one of the underwater saga of Argo, a series which ran for several years.

Nat Brand, the possibly Scots strip cartoonist, added another excellently drawn hero to his gallery of greats with Argo. Here he proved to be as excellent a depicter of undersea creatures as he was those from outer

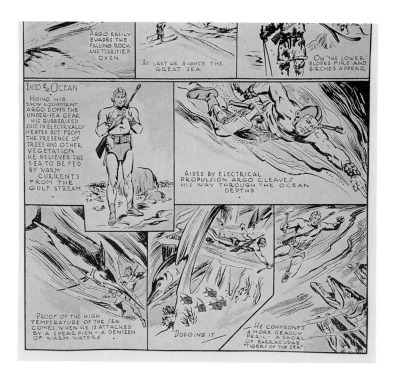

ARGO
UNDER the OCEAN

A FISH, BEARING A GOLDEN TABLET HAS BEEN CAUGHT AND PRESENTED TO A WELL KNOWN MUSEUM.
SENSATIONAL FOR A TIME BUT SOON FORGOTTEN BY THE PUBLIC.
ONE MAN, A DARING ADVENTURER, AND FAMOUS INVENTOR DETERMINES TO PUT HIS UNDER-SEA INVENTIONS TO THE SUPREME TEST.

THE STRANGE FISH BEARING A GOLDEN TABLET

ARGO FAMOUS INVENTOR

THE GOLDEN TABLET

HIGH OVER THE ARCTIC WASTES ARGO SPEEDS ON HIS WAY.

LANDING IN A SHELTERED SPOT WHEN HIS FUEL GIVES OUT HE CONTINUES HIS QUEST ON SKIS

WEARY DAYS OF TRUDGING THROUGH BITTER STORMS.

ENLIVENED BY BREATHLESS ESCAPES FROM HUNGRY POLAR BEARS

ENCOUNTERS WITH WOLVES

MORE DESPERATE STILL HE SWEEPS OVER A RISE, INTO A CIRCLE OF MENACING MUSK OXEN

SUPER SCIENCE THRILLS

by A.R.G.
(1945) International Publications (Edinburgh)

Super Science Thrills was the first all sci-fi comic-book published in Britain. It stemmed, in fact, from Edinburgh and was completely drawn by an artist who signed himself A.R.G. There were three main strips, 'In Search of Atlantis', which took the front and back pages to tell of how a couple called David and Jim set off in their wonderful one-man submarines to find the lost land of Atlantis. Deep in the dark ocean they save a tribe of man-like creatures from monsters and wind up as guests of the Queen of Atlantis. After a slap-up feast of fish food, they sub back home as bearers of a casket of pearls! Other strips are 'The Time Travellers in Back to the Stone Age', and 'Cruise of the Spacebird', in which young Bobby and Irene take a trip to the moon with their Uncle, 'the famous scientist'. Once there they meet monsters, moon men, and the Moon Master, who presents them with handfuls of diamonds to take home. Sounds familiar?

A.R.G., evidently as Scottish as his publishers, contributed to a number of locally produced comics, including *Happijack*, a small oblong comic, and a new edition of *Ally Sloper's Half Holiday*.

SUPER SCIENCE THRILLS

In Search of Atlantis
by ARG

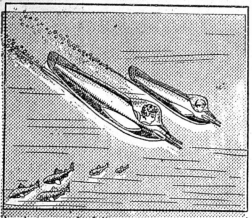

In their wonderful one-man, atomic powered submarines, David and Jim set off in their search for the lost land of Atlantis.

Legends tell of Atlantis sinking to the bottom of the sea, thousands of years ago. As the chums reach the dark depths of the ocean, strange luminous fish appear.

Suddenly a huge waving tentacle seizes the leading submarine. Jim has been captured by some awful deep-sea monster.

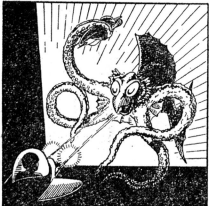

In the glare of his searchlight, David sees the ferocious creature. Fearlessly he attacks. His blazing guns pump radio-active bullets into his foe.

With Jim free once more, they sail on through the deep. Suddenly they see a cluster of strange lights milling around below them.

Diving to investigate, they see a number of strange little man-like creatures being attacked by two huge fish.

They dive in, with guns firing. Nothing can withstand the radio-active bullets, and the savage fish are soon killed.

THE MOON MAN

by W. Forshaw
***Zip-Bang Comic* (1946)**
W. Forshaw (Liverpool)

In a space-ship fifty miles above the Earth hovers the Moon Man, saying to himself, 'It is some days since I was on the Earth. I will go down and see if I can find some adventure.' As he flies through the skies, he remarks, 'It's good to flash through the clouds again!' Scarcely has he landed when he hears a gunshot and the scream of a woman. A gang of crooks have kidnapped the inventor of a secret ray! 'Moon Man will soon destroy these criminals!' he tells the distraught daughter, and flies after the crooks' car. To get the professor's secret, the crooks plan to ram a red-hot needle under his finger nails. 'Y-you devils!' cries the prof. 'Moan!' But the Moon Man arrives, crying 'I'm the Man from the Moon!' The crooks are not nonplussed. Indeed, they are plussed, for one replies, 'Meet the ex-heavyweight champion of Ireland!' After much hand-to-hand fighting and a struggle with a lady crook with short skirts and a neckline to match, Moon Man restores the prof to his daughter and flies home. 'Great Scot!' gasps a bobby, 'th-th-they're whizzin' into space!'

A super-hero or a sci-fi star? This early alien from outer space qualifies as both. The comic was the second in the *Zip* series edited and produced by W. Forshaw of Liverpool. An advertisement promoted the next two comics, *Zip-Zing* and *Zip-Zoom*, but to date neither of these titles has been traced.

A TRIP TO MARS

by Bob Wilkin
***Big Parade Comic* (1947)**
Grant Hughes Ltd (London)

A spaceship from Earth is making the first trip to the planet Mars, piloted by the uniformed Crane. On board are Clive and Ruth. The dauntless trio need no oxygen masks as they explore the surface after a bumpy landing, but are quickly captured by a group of thuggish but non-speaking Martians. Clive gets himself tortured and patched up with a torn sheet. Then they are taken before the headman, who tells them, 'You Earth people have no right to be on Mars. You shall die for your foolishness!' But there is one hope left – Crane's power drill – if it still works! 'I'll connect it up to the light switch,' says Crane, and they quickly drill their way out of their rocky jail. Then it's back to the spaceship – 'We're in luck – the old bus still works!' and they are off, back to Mother Earth!

This simple tale of spacemen and Martians was told in his crisp and clean style by Bob Wilkin, one of the stalwarts of Forties British comic-books. In the same comic, all sixteen pages of which were by Wilkin, he presents 'Dean of the Undersea Patrol', and more interestingly, 'Homer the Manbat', a jungle superman who turns up at the end of a three-page thriller in time to save Grace and Ron from fierce natives. *Big Parade*, a typical one-shot, was printed in alternate pages of red-and-black on shiny-sided beige paper.

BIG PARADE COMIC

PRICE 6D

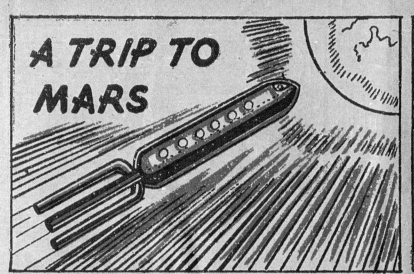

THE AMPHIBASTRA

by Crewe Davies
***New Worlds Comic* (1947)**
Cardal Publishing Co (Manchester)

'There are many strange places on Earth yet to be reached by man… but to penetrate these regions means the formation of costly expeditions. For this reason Ken Pentard, an inventor, had been experimenting on an All Purpose Vehicle which would fly, float on, and go under water, travel over land, and bore like a mole through the Earth. As he completes the machine, we join him in his workshop to witness The Test of the Amphibastra!' So much for preamble. Next morning Ken and his mechanic Lefty O'Mally, 'the best mechanic from out of Oiland', take off. Little do they know that stowed away are Ken's younger brother and sister, schoolboy Pip and schoolgirl Diana! Soon they are zooming over the coast at 2800 mph, and five hours later arrive at the South Pole. Thanks to the added weight of the kids, the Amphibastra crashes into the icy Antarctic where hundreds of little Bubble-men float the ship into a fluorescent cavern. They are greeted by a creature named Yatso, better known to sailors as Davy Jones! Odder things follow, including the defeat by Ken of a monstrous whale – he boils it! – before they return to the normal world.

Crewe Davies was quite a quirky sci-fi star among comic artists. One of the new post-war breed, he also drew 'Crash Britanus the World Crime Buster', and 'Dane Jerrus of the Interplanetary Solar Force'.

Published by Cardal Publishing Co., Ltd., 83 Ducie Street, M/c. 1—Printed by A.A.P. Ltd., M/c. 4.

BURT STEELE AND SATIN ASTRO: IN THE YEAR 3000 AD

by Dennis M. Reader
Whizzer Comics **(1947)** *Super Duper Comics* **(1948)**
Cartoon Art Productions (Glasgow)

'Discovered and brought to life by Dennis M. Reader' was the byline to the opening episode of this series of sci-fi strips. It began with 'Note', which read: 'This story was found in the year 4000 AD in a time capsule, sealed by a space adventurer, Burt Steele. He chronicled many of his adventures, and was believed to have died at the hands of Lamarr, Warlord of Mars.' The story then started, captioned in the first person: 'Straight as an arrow my rocket plane shot from Earth. I felt good, high in the stratosphere… alone… or as I thought…' A voice says hello, and – 'Jeepers! Satin Astro!' Steele has aboard an escaped criminal, a very glamorous one. She has eluded the Earth Police and their bad boss Krozac, and now hijacks Steele's rocket to fly to Planet Xnay, 'a modern Devil's Island', where her band of Rocket Pirates have been exiled. Steele turns out to be on her side, and soon they are breaking the bad girls out of Blak Jale, where nasty guards have been torturing them ('How's dis electric whip feel, huh?'). It is the start of a series of double-act adventures with Steele and the luscious Satin.

Dennis M. Reader, the eighteen-year-old left-handed cartoonist, had a great love for American comic-books and, indeed, the American way of life. Even the 'M' in his name was an American-style affectation, inserted for effect only. He created many characters for the Scots publisher, Cartoon Art Productions and their CAP-toon Comics, most of them super-heroes. See the companion book, *Super Duper Supermen!*

IT'S SUPER DUPER COMICS

BRITISH 1/- ISSUE

NO. 13

BURT STEELE AND SATIN ASTRO in — "Adventure on the Dust Planet"

THE FIGHT FOR THE MOON

by George Blow
Jupiter Adventure Comic **(1947)**
Scoop Books (Glasgow)

'In the year 3000 AD the men of Jupiter are attacking the Moon, who radio the Earth for help. Professor Blake and Buck Duban arrive on the Moon with their latest invention, the vibro-disintegrater.' This sci-fi adventure seems to be well under way as the Prof and Buck arrive in the first picture, no rocket-ship in sight. The Jupiter-men step out of an airlocked cave and set horned apes on to the Earthmen. They rig up their vibrogun, but two watch-apes capture them. The head Jupiter-man points out their position, in English, of course. 'We are in possession of the Moon, the people are drowning, we have let in the waters, you will be left here and the cave door shut!' But the evil leader reckons without the moon-rats who, according to the caption, 'have a taste for Earth rope!' They gnaw our chaps free. It is the work of a moment to block a flooding tunnel with boulders dislodged by their Vibro-ray, for Buck to bop a watch-ape, and for Moon City to be saved! The Moon Men are delighted: 'Please accept this gift – radioactive rock which will give power for 12,000 years!' All that remains to be said is, 'Goodbye, Earthmen!' The End.

A one-shot eight-pager from a Scottish publisher, via Scottish cartoonists. Apart from George Blow's fairly incoherent work, the comic also featured 'Porky Peters, the Fat Boy of Popple's College', and 'Nixon Dott the Terrible Tec'.

EVIL ISLAND

by Rex Hart
***Top Mark Adventures* (1947)**
Foldes Modern Printing Service (Edinburgh)

'**C**rikey!! What's that?' cried Bob, or possibly Jack, as Jack and Bob escape from a shipwreck and get cast up on the rocky shores of Evil Island. 'It's prehistoric!' answers Jack, or possibly Bob, as they duck into a handy cave. They avoid a giant prehistoric lizard and a swooping pterodactyl, only to be greeted by a more modern horror, gun-shots and a bespectacled Professor. 'My henchmen are too quick on the draw!' he apologises, taking them to a comfortably furnished room in the cave where they are fed fruit and cakes by Karina, the Prof's pretty niece. There follows an escorted tour of the island. 'You are the only strangers to have seen my preparations for an assault against the world,' says the Prof. 'Here is my fleet of supersonic planes!' Later in bed, Jack, or possibly Bob, sums up. 'That chap's a dangerous madman!' he says. Next morning the Prof demonstrates his new Radium Wave from a flying plane: 'Makes the Atom Bomb look like a toy!' he laughs, as he blows up the next-door island. Next he tells the boys they will be the first to learn the powers of his new anti-personnel device. He pulls a lever marked Anti-Personnel and the lads' chair-arms close on them with a vice-like grip. 'Now you will be electrocuted as soon as I press the button!' chuckles the Prof. Fortunately niece Karina switches the thing off and they make a dash for it, over the Leaden Bridge and into the Prof's patent plane. Then it's *bang! zoom!* and away. 'So ends the threat of Evil Island!' says Bob, or was it Jack?

'Matt Hardy, Special Investigator' took the main credit on the cover of *Top Mark Adventures*, although the splash picture showed the Professor's strange henchmen firing their X-Gun at the escaping rocket-plane. Also in this twelve-page, oddly coloured one-shot was 'Java the Jungle Brave', a Tarzan-type who rescues some orchid hunters with his curious cry of *'Aaoohee!!'*

ASTRA: THE MYSTERY AIR ACE

Zoom **(1947)**
Children's Press (Glasgow)

Astra the Mystery Air Ace, front and back page star of the *Zoom* comic, was described as 'This masked pilot is ready to take on any death-defying mission at a moment's notice. His 'plane is the last word in jets!' Astra's adventures begin with a briefcase. 'That wallet contains world-shaking secrets!' says a mysterious man. Astra gives his word that it will be delivered to the Military Authorities without fail. 'His word is his bond.' Exactly why this trip from airfield to authority should take so long, especially as he is flying the world's latest and fastest jet-plane, is unclear, but Astra remarks to himself, behind the veil of a blue handkerchief, 'Another five hours flying time and I'll be there!' Suddenly a midget plane makes straight for his tail – 'Now turn to Back Page!' – followed by two more. Astra tries to shake them off, then realises that they are radio-controlled! Spotting a nearby radio station, Astra destroys it by dumping his spare petrol tank on the hut, then exploding it with tracer bullets. And so Astra foils the members of an International Gang and gets the wallet of documents to HQ, dead on time!

Zoom was one of several high-quality comic-books published by the Glasgow-based Children's Press. They all cost fourpence, a penny more than the average comic of the day. Edited by Frederick Chaplain, a former Amalgamated Press editor, *Zoom* also included 'Young Tornado', a 'lithe, skin-clad figure' from the Amazon jungles, drawn by Bob Mortimer, plus 'The Moonites', an alien invasion cartoon by Denis Gifford.

THE ATOMIC AGE COMIC

**by Walter Booth and Stanley White
(1947) L. Burn & Co (Newcastle-on-Tyne)**

This was the first all-science fiction comic-book to be published in Britain since the small eight-pager, *Super Science Thrills*. A much more impressive affair, it contained thirty-six pages and cost one shilling (five pence). The main feature strip was 'Speeding Through Space', subtitled 'A Story of Speed, Power and Peril in the Atomic Age'. This starred Rex Rogers, a young athlete, scientist and airman, and Professor Ingram, inventor and builder of 'a great space ship driven by atomic energy'. Having picked up a television transmission from Mars starring Princess Zornea, they are up and away in moments: 'It is only a hundred and forty million miles!' says the Prof. Centrifugal energy is switched on to oppose the gravitation of Mars and act as a brake. 'We won't need oxygen helmets!' smiles Rex. Soon the chaps are roped by glamorous Amazons, but their scientific superiority helps vanquish an attack by Barbarians – they divert the lava from an erupting volcano. Returning to Earth, they bring Princess Zornea along for a holiday trip! This long adventure ran for thirteen packed pages.

Hugh Stanley White, one of the first comic artists to specialise in science-fiction, drew 'Ian on Mu' for *Mickey Mouse Weekly* back in 1936. Walter Booth originated adventure strips in British comics as early as 1920, drawing 'Rob the Rover' in *Puck*. White had been Booth's young assistant, and now the two old friends got together to produce this unique comic-book. Other picture strips included 'Dick Gordon the Man-Bat' and 'Jungle Zarton' by White, and 'The Death Daring Duvals' and 'Atomic Tommy the Bullet Proof Crime Smasher' by Booth. Unfortunately, the Newcastle printer mixed up the pages, making the comic quite difficult to read!

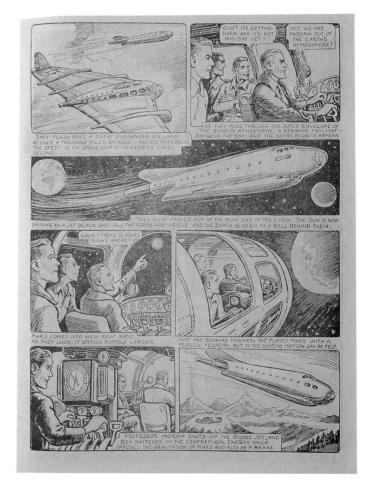

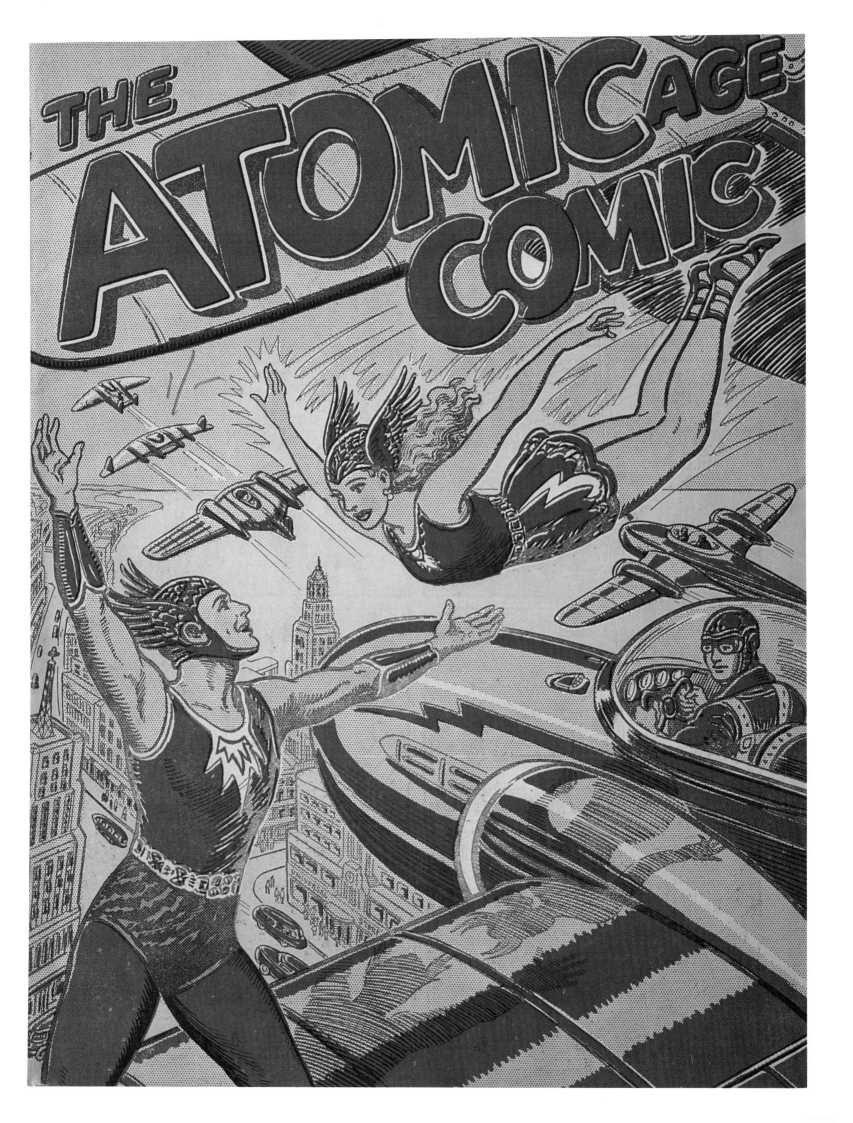

SPACE ROAMERS

by R. Plummer
Big Time, Big Show, Big Chief, Big Shot (1947)
Scion Ltd (London)

'The Adventures of Reg and his Friends in the Craters of the Moon' began on the front and back pages of *Big-Time Comic*, continued in *Big Show Comic* as 'Space Flyers', carried on in *Big Chief Comic* as 'Space Rovers', and concluded in *Big Shot Comic* as 'Space Rovers', too – evidently artist Plummer ran out of variant titles. The two Roamers were Reg and his father, who 'has been perfecting a huge rocket-propelled craft designed to take long journeys into interplanetary space.' All set to go to the Moon, Dad tells young Reg, 'This is my surprise for you – you're coming with us!' 'Gee, thanks Dad!' says Reg. The rocket soars away from Earth at 78 miles per second, and as an added slice of science to the fiction, a caption explains that 'they must land on the Moon between sun and shadow so as not to get the full glare of the sun, which would burn them up, there being no air blanket to absorb the sun's rays.' Illustrating current technology, the rocket turns 'backside-foremost' in order to settle on its tail. 'This is necessary to enable them to take off again when leaving.' Dad and Reg jump the sixty feet to the surface, 'floating down gently as though falling through water on the Earth.' We are now bidden to turn to the back page, where all pretence at science is suddenly lost as 'huge disc-like creatures, shining with a pinkish glow as though made of mother of pearl', come racing towards them. A quick blast with Reg's electron gun splinters the discs into fragments, and they go roaring home to Earth in time for the last panel, where 'Dad and Reg have great difficulty in making the family believe their experience on the Moon!'

Serialised over several one-shot comics, the adventures of the Space Roamers/Flyers/Rovers were the first strips to have a solid basis in science before taking off into fiction. The second adventure opened with 'So-long, Mum, we're off to the Moon again!'; the third with 'Reg and his father are off in their rocket to Mars'; and the fourth with Reg saying 'I'll try and bring you something beautiful back from Venus, Sis!' He does – it is the colourful wing of a Venusian sucker-fly!

BIG-TIME! COMIC 3ᴰ

NEP

SPACE ROAMERS

THE ADVENTURES OF REG. AND HIS FRIENDS IN THE CRATERS OF THE MOON

THE CREW ARE ALL SET TO GO—TO THE MOON FIRST—AND THIS IS MY SURPRISE FOR YOU; YOU'RE COMING WITH US!

GEE! THANKS, DAD!

Reg's father has been perfecting a huge rocket propelled craft, designed to take long journeys into interplanetary space. To Reg's joy, Dad says he may accompany them on their first journey—to the MOON.

WE MUST LAND ON THE SHADOW'S EDGE—WE SHALL BE THERE VERY SHORTLY

They rapidly approach the Moon and Dad explains to Reg that they must land on the Moon between sun and shadow so as not to get the full glare of the sun, which would burn them up, there being no 'air blanket' to absorb the sun's rays.

GO ON, REG—JUMP OUT LIKE THE OTHERS—IT'S QUITE SAFE TO DO IT. GRAVITY IS LESS ON THE MOON!

SO REG IS FITTED WITH A SPACE-SUIT LIKE THE REST OF THE CREW AND THE GIANT ROCKET ROARS AWAY FROM THE EARTH AT 78 MILES PER SECOND!

REVERSING IT'S POSITION IN SPACE THE BIG ROCKET DROPS CAREFULLY BACK-WARDS DOWN TO THE MOON'S SURFACE

The Rocket turns 'backside-foremost' in order to settle on its tail. This is necessary to enable them to 'take off' again when leaving.

HERE WE ARE REG, ACTUALLY ON THE MOON. WE'LL TAKE A LOOK INSIDE THAT CRATER OVER THERE FIRST—

NEP

The crew jump out from a height of 60 feet to the ground, and float down gently, as though falling through water on the earth. They find miles of mineral dust interspersed with craters and decide to explore a little.

SEE BACK PAGE

DANE JERRUS: AGENT ONE OF THE INTERPLANETARY SOLAR FORCE

by Crewe Davies
***Super Duper Comics* (1948)**
Cartoon Art Productions (Glasgow)

Dane Jerrus, Agent One, and his sidekick Chummy Brown, were lying around the bar of the Space Landing Cradles on the ultra-cold side of Mercury, 'hoping to solve the latest mystery of the void', as their adventures began in No. 8 of *Super Duper Comics*. 'The 1945 freighter from old Earth is due today,' remarks Dane. 'Let's go see, huh?' But something's wrong. Using his mighty strength to force an entry into the silent ship, Dane discovers the crew frozen into statues. 'Jeeze!' he remarks, and as to the ship's cargo – 'Blimey! It's gone!' A second freighter, the 'U235 Otto', is due, too, so Dane and Chummy jet off in their space-scooter. Too late, they watch as pirate ships use magnetic grips to rob the Otto: 'There goes a hundred million quid, Chummy!' Following the pirates to their base, Dane leaps forth. 'With no pressure-suit and not enough time to dress in one, the Superman of the Solar Force has five minutes to win or die!' Then – 'Holy Mac!' cries Dane as he comes face to face with the chief pirate, who is well christened 'The Horror'! Finally Dane explains all: 'When turned on to a space freighter which was travelling faster than light, the Freeze Ray froze the image of the ship that was behind-time of the vessel. In this way the frozen replica of the real ship continued on course until atmosphere thawed or melted it!' Or, as Dane Jerrus, master of linguistics, added, 'Jeepers!'

Crewe Davies's superhero of the spaceways had a three-year run in the Scottish occasional, *Super Duper Comics*. He made several coloured cover appearances starting with No. 12, an illustration from the interior adventure, 'Devil's Moon'.

SWIFT MORGAN

by Denis McLoughlin
Swift Morgan **(1948)**
T.V. Boardman Ltd (London)

'**S**wift and Silver, aboard a new rocket air-ship, are in grave danger when out of control, their ship plunges towards a lake in unchartered (*sic*) territory at terrific speed.' Soon the intrepid explorers were up to their photogravure necks in prehistoric orange-and-green monsters. 'By the!' gasped Speed, self-censoringly, 'A flesh-eating tyrant dinosaur!' Did he mean tyrranosaur? Script apart, it was a great visual beginning for a six-year run of occasional comic-books that took Swift and Silver (she was identified in issue No. 2 as his fiancée) to Ancient Rome, Ancient Egypt, and up the Osumacinta River to a Lost City of the Incas. They took off into space in a later twelve-page episode entitled 'Swift Morgan and the Flying Saucers', via Professor Dwight Mooney's rocket-ship, a 35,000,000 mile journey into the unknown. Two hundred and fifty days later they land on Mars: 'I see the canal theory is correct!' muses the Prof. After many adventures Swift saves the captive Silver from Emperor Meturas of Martinia and the midget Martians from a Saturnite invasion.

The most popular space hero of his period, Swift Morgan was created and drawn by Denis McLoughlin, a brilliant artist who also painted the full-colour covers for T.V. Boardman's many paperbacks and dust-jacketed novels. The scripts were written by his brother, Colin McLoughlin.

THE ADVENTURES OF
SWIFT MORGAN
and the
FLYING SAUCERS
3d
CUTTING FROM THE "DAILY MAIL"
NEW YORK, TUESDAY.—An article in the American magazine True claims that eight months' investigation has shown that "flying saucers" reported seen in all parts of the world were "space vehicles" from another planet which has been watching the earth.
WHITE SANDS, NEW MEXICO, WITH ITS VAST DESERT AND CLEAR BLUE SKY HAS OFTEN PROVED ITSELF EXCELLENT AS A ROCKET RESEARCH AND EXPERIMENTAL STATION. IT IS NEAR HERE, IN THE ISOLATED WASTELANDS THAT WE FIND SWIFT MORGAN AND SILVER PREPARING TO TAKE A NEW SUPER-JET AIRCRAFT OUT ON A TEST FLIGHT. PROFESSOR DWIGHT MOONEY, INVENTOR OF THE SECRET PLANE, IS GIVING LAST MINUTE INSTRUCTIONS TO SWIFT. . . . . . .
ILLUSTRATED BY D MC LOUGHLIN. STORY BY C. MC LOUGHLIN.

SWIFT MORGAN SPACE COMIC

by Denis McLoughlin
(1953) Popular Press Ltd (London)

'**S**wift Morgan on the Planet of Destiny' was the leading feature in this new sixpenny comic-book, which was subtitled 'Fast Action on the Worlds of the Future!' We discover Swift and his lady, Silver, as Captain and Hostess on one of the spaceline's largest interplanetary ships. They are *en route* for Mars in Swift's specially designed minicruiser, Blue Light. 'We'll soon be getting a nice spacetan relaxing on the artificial beach at Montula!' says Silver. Suddenly an explosion wrecks both their plans and the Blue Light, and they are captured by Commander Tunis, 'OC of all destinal research for Dictator Jodd of Jupiter'. Communication is made easy by electrically-wired mind antennae. 'Oh, Swift! Is – is it the end of the whole solar system?' gasps Silver. Not with our long-established hero at hand. 'Steady, Silver!' he says. With the help of Strang, a saurian barbarian of the Booloo Tribe, the handsome Earthlings duly explode the artificial Planet of Destiny and rocket home aboard the spaceship 'Observer One'.

The increasing popularity of the American reprint comic-book, a sixpenny black-and-white stapled into a full-colour cover, prompted T.V. Boardman to discontinue their line of threepenny photogravure comics and launch a new series in the new format. Denis McLoughlin proved to be as fine a black-and-white artist as he was in colour. His back-up feature was a new hero, 'Sam English – Museum Rover,' an interplanetary adventurer based on the sub-tropical island of Mentos. Sam had his 'Silver', too, in the shape of Miss Vel Burrows, a sexy secretary who shares his adventures.

REX COSMO: COSMIC SCIENTIST

***Scoops Comic* (1948)**
Hotspur Publishing Co (Manchester)

Rex Cosmo, 'wonder scientist of the year AD 2000', picks up an SOS from his earthbound assistant, Stella Vane. He is returning home in his spaceship 'Thunderbolt' with a cargo of Xranium ore, when aerial pirates attack. Grabbing his space-kit and propulsion unit, the scientist soars off in search of the pirates, who are using a strange magnetic force to jam the Thunderbolt's atomic motors. Rex Cosmo's ray-gun glows as it discharges crackling jets at the armoured pirate, crippling it. As the attack continues, Rex makes for the planet Pluto, but on landing is confronted by Zek, captain of the Martian pirates. 'Welcome to Pluto, Earthman!' he sneers. Problems mount as the local inhabitants, 'Pluto Giants, huge aboriginal brutes glowing with metallic light', enter the scene. These Zombies, as they are known, prise open the Xranium canister and are promptly paralysed by deadly radiations. Reinforced by his Cosmic Energiser, Rex knocks out the last Zombie with a cosmic-powered punch. 'Refuel the Thunderbolt, Stella!' he cries jubilantly. 'We've seen the last of the Martian Pirates and the Zombies of Pluto!'

This eight-page red-and-blue comic-book was entirely the work of the same artist who drew *Prang Comic* for the same Mancunian publisher (see *Super Duper Supermen!*). Unfortunately he failed to sign his work. Back-up strips in *Scoops* were 'The Gunsmoke Kid', a western, and 'Jerry Flynn the Crime Chaser'.

1. Rex Cosmo, wonder scientist of the Year A.D. 2000, picks up an S.O.S. from his assistant Stella Vane, returning to Earth with a cargo of Xranium ore in the space ship "Thunderbolt."

2. Grabbing his space-kit and propulsion unit, the scientist soars off in search of the aerial pirates, propelled by the supercharged cosmic energiser, Cosmo's latest discovery.

3. Stella locates the pirate ship attempting to ram the "Thunderbolt." She takes avoiding action, but her instruments show the enemy ship is using a strange magnetic force to jam the "Thunderbolt's" atomic motors.

4. Moving with lightning speed, Cosmo arrives, his ray-gun glowing as it discharges crackling jets at the armoured hull of the pirate ship, which retreats in face of the onslaught.

5. As the enemy space-ship drifts out-of-control, its motors crippled, Cosmo swoops across to the "Thunderbolt," cruising steadily back on her course.

6. The scientist climbs through the pressure chamber into the control room of the "Thunderbolt" just as the lights on the instrument panel flicker. The enemy ship is in action again!

THOR: RULER OF A STRANGE WORLD

by Philip Mendoza
The Mighty Atom **(1948)**
Denlee Publishing Co (London)

'Every year, hundreds of people are reported missing. Many are never heard of again. What happens to them? Could it be that...' And so begin the adventures which befall Bill and Mary one afternoon in a Surrey lane. A spaceship lands and a horde of bouncing Frogmen carry the couple off to a strange planet where they are taken before Chang the Ruler. 'I have lived here many centuries, as you count time. Here it does not exist,' explains Chang. 'Then came Thor, Master of Evil. He would make this planet a Kingdom of the Damned!' Mazoor the Black takes Bill and Mary to Chang's secret stronghold, but little do they know he is a traitor! He takes them through a dense thicket of carnivorous plants, but Bill thwarts the hungry tentacles by setting fire to his blazer, which may be the first time a blazer actually lived up to its name! Captured by Thor's Thin-men, the Earthchums are lashed hand and foot to Execution Poles, where they are forced to watch the Red Dwarf perform the ritual Dance of Death. Suddenly the Frogmen bounce in, ray-guns ablast, saving our toothsome twosome who escape with little more damage than tastefully ripped shirts and shorts. 'What part will Bill and Mary play in the forthcoming struggle? Order your next copy of *The Mighty Atom* now!' I did – and I'm still waiting!

The Mighty Atom, subtitled 'The British Illustrated', was the largest format, best coloured, best drawn comic produced in its day, yet it failed to survive beyond its No. 1. Perhaps at sixpence it was too expensive for the children of the Forties. The comic was entirely drawn by Philip Mendoza, one of the best artists ever to work in comics, and was edited and written by Stephen Frances, who is now better known as the original 'Hank Janson', author of so very many sleazy crime-and-sex paperbacks of the period.

The MIGHTY ATOM
6d.
THE BRITISH ILLUSTRATED
PACKED WITH THRILLS & ADVENTURE!
BILL NEVISON HIGHWAYMAN
GAT WILLIAMS — GANG BUSTER AND CURLY, HIS ASSISTANT
THE OKLAHOMA KID ROBIN HOOD OF THE PURPLE SAGE
THOR
SINISTER RULER OF A STRANGE PLANET.
Drawings by Mendoza
Edited by S. Frances

THE METEOR

cover by Nat Brand
(1948) Children's Press (Glasgow)

The Meteor, subtitled 'A Budget of Adventure, Fantasy and Fun', was, as the exciting cover predicted, essentially a sci-fi comic. Its twenty pages (price sixpence) included 'Challenge from Space' and 'Zeno at the Earth's Core', both four-page adventure strips coloured red and black. The first story told of RAF jets being brought down by invaders from a Pirate Planet. 'Calling all Earth Men – our rocket legions are ready to attack. You have 48 Earth hours to surrender!' When further planes fail, the CO sends for Professor Porter, who takes off in his home-made rocketship, piloted by Tiny Tugwell, the RAF six-footer! They spot a rocket from the mystery planet and follow it home to Vega. Tiny Tugwell soon deals with a monstrous reptile – he conks it with his oar! – and the planet itself is destroyed by an onrush from Comet X. Luckily our lads manage to blast off in time! Further on, 'Zeno at the Earth's Core' illustrates how scientist Neil Hammond and his 'Ocean Belle', 'the most modern diving apparatus ever invented', takes a trip down the Mindanao Deep. 'It's a new world, Corky!' he says to his assistant, young Corky McCormack, who answers 'Crikey!' Then they meet Zeno, Lord of the Inner Circle, the Unknown World in the centre of the Earth. Zeno explains: 'The Inner Circle is an air bubble separated from the flames of the core by silica and metallic oxides, vitrified into glass by the flame's heat.' But Neil doesn't trust Zeno, and through the agency of Marko, an inventor, Neil and Corky return to the surface in Marko's amazing asbestos 'Screwbore', a revolving vehicle. 'It's just like a corkscrew!' laughs Corky.

Mallard Features, a Scots comic strip agency run by ex-D.C. Thomson artist, William McCail, packaged this comic-book for the Children's Press. 'Challenge from Space' was anonymous, but 'Zeno at the Earth's Core' was by Alf Farningham.

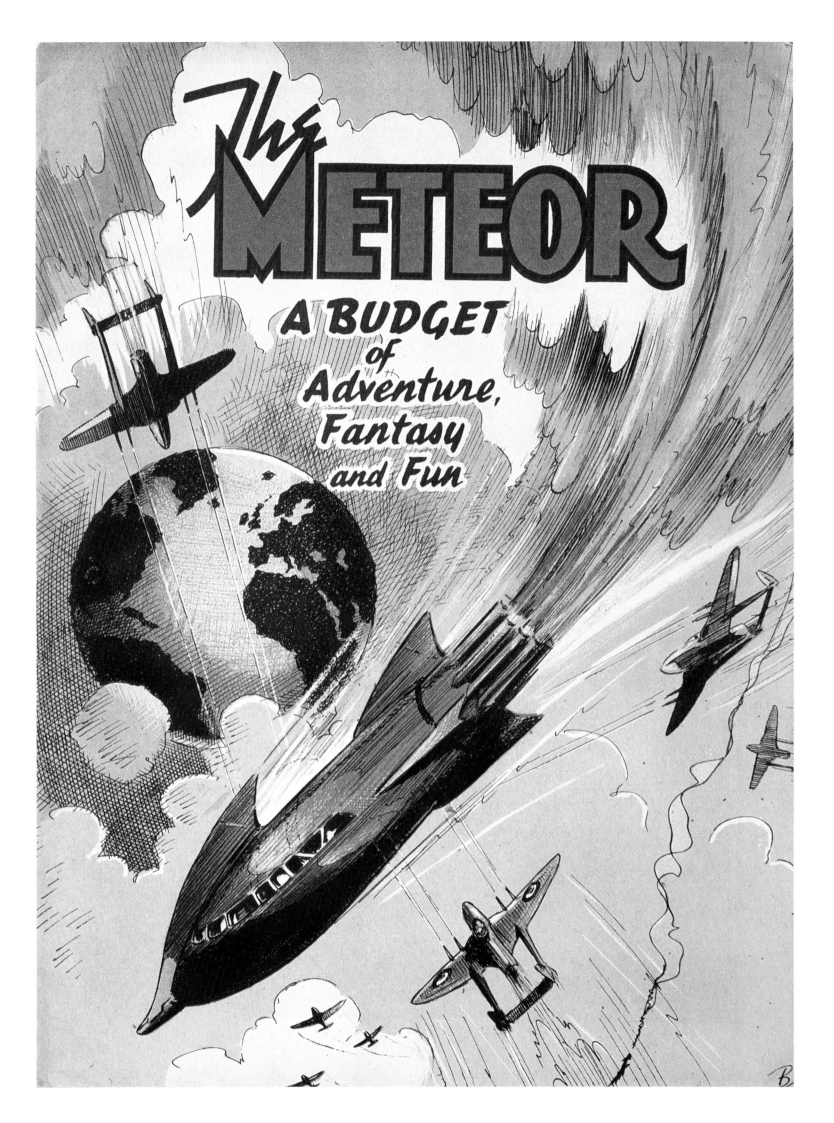

THE ATOMIC MOLE

by Ron Turner
Big Scoop, Big Atlantis, Big Ranch **(1949)**
Scion Ltd (London)

'Professor Jeans, Rip Rivers and his son Jim are off to explore subterranean caverns that the Professor calculates lie some 75 miles down. Their boring machine, The Mole, employs atomic destructor tubes.' Sixteen hours and two pictures after this preamble, 'The Mole' crashes through into a fantastic new world. 'Light and heat seem to come from lava pouring into that ravine there!' observes young sonny Jim. 'Yes, pity the air isn't purer!' adds Dad. Suddenly a sinister black shape wings overhead and grabs 'The Mole' – a flying lizard! Rip Rivers shoots it and they are dropped into a lake of boiling water. 'You look like a hard-boiled egg coming up for the third time, Prof!' laughs Rip as they swim ashore. Using a nearby diplodocus to haul 'The Mole' out of the pond, their troubles seem to be over. But no! 'Down the gully streams an army of huge ant-like creatures, armed to the jaws!' Some rapid shooting, and 'bellowing violently', the Mole returns to the surface and home. 'I'm spending a quiet week-end in the garden, digging!' the Prof tells the press.

The opening three pages of this series began in *Big Scoop Comic*, the lead feature of which was a tale of how reporter Scoop Granger foiled a Black Market racket. This was also drawn by Ron Turner, a new talent in comics but one which would soon make a major mark. *Big Atlantis Comic* followed, with the Prof, Rip and Jim discovering Lost Atlantis 1400 miles beneath the Earth's crust. Finally there were more adventures of The Atomic Mole in *Big Ranch Comic*.

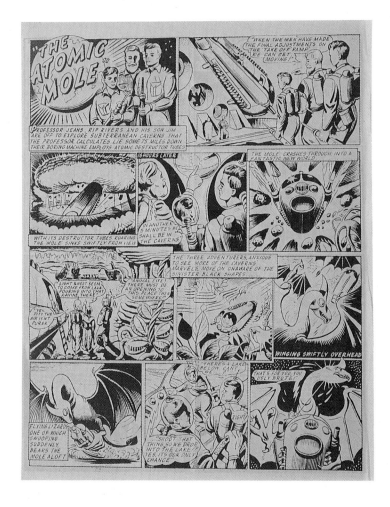

PAT PERIL: THE FEARLESS FIGHTER OF THE FUTURE

by Bob Monkhouse
Modern Comics **(1949)**
Modern Fiction Ltd (London)

'Through the vastness of outer space hurtles the Terra rocket-ship of Pat Peril, pioneer investigator for the Universal Police! With him travels Nimrod, his Martian pet.' They are off to the Land of the Lizard via an unknown constellation ('Groo!' grumbles Nimrod the Martian pet) when – 'Great Jupiter!' – the planet they are passing has an atmosphere of nitrogen! 'That means our rockets won't burn in it! We'll come to a stop!' Quickly Pat releases a parachute to prevent the crash, and straps on his oxygen mask as he leaps from the ship. A hasty examination reveals that the planet's soil contains glycerine, which means that oxygen in the atmosphere would blow it up. Suddenly monster lizards attack Pat, but he has the solution. 'I'll climb this hill – reptiles don't like heights!' Racing back to the ship he calls Nimrod to tear out the fuel-tubes and put oxygen cans in their place! 'Schmh?' queries Nimrod, but 'within seconds the fresh air pours from the rocket, combines with the chemicals of the strange world, and blows the ship into outer space, killing the monsters!' Pat ejects an oxygen cylinder into a glycerine lake, creating one of man's greatest bombs – nitro-glycerine! 'There goes the biggest mine in the universe!' laughs Pat Peril as he flies on, 'keeping the spaceways clear and safe for civilisation!'

Excitingly drawn by Bob Monkhouse, 'Pat Peril' was the front page hero of *Modern Comics*, one of a series of one-shot three-penny books which I edited for Modern Fiction. Its companion, *Amazing Comics*, is featured in our own companion, *Super Duper Supermen!*

ACE ROGERS

by Alf Farningham
Comic Adventures **(1949)**
A. Soloway Ltd (London)

'**M**eet Ace Rogers in his new adventure. In his Planet Plane with Mark Logran and a picked crew he plans to be the first Earthman to land on the Moon!' A startling twist to the life of the long-lived hero who had started out as 'Ace Rogers of the Submarine Salvo' back in the wartime pages of *Comic Adventures* in 1943. After several successful sorties against the Nazis and the Japanese, Ace's demobbed adventures began in 1946 when he set out to locate 'The Lost Gold of the Incas' in Professor Marton's amphibious submarine, 'The Platypus'. From then on sci-fi was the watchword, and in the final (Volume 7, No. 2) issue of *Comic Adventures*, Ace set forth, in full colour for the first time, for the Moon. The Planet Plane is forced off course by a strange power, and crash-lands on a hitherto unknown world where Vlaga, Leader of the Men of Thought, explains all. Ace's spaceship was trapped in Vlaga's magnetic waves, as the first step in his plan to conquer Earth. Already his platoons of Mindless Men are labouring on a Cylindrical Machine which will bring death and destruction to Earth. At the end of the episode, hope springs as Ace encounters Partha the Peaceful and his plans to overthrow Vlaga. 'How will Ace fare?' Alas, we would never know.

The last issue of Soloway's famous fourpenny burst into full colour to celebrate. Unfortunately the printer, unused to such extravagance, got his plates mixed, so that on his last page, Ace Hart and Co appear with green faces instead of pink!

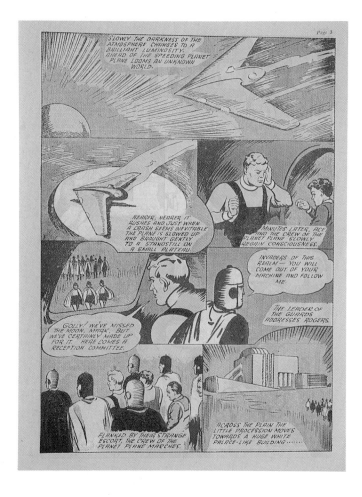

COMIC Adventures

Vol. VII   No. 2   4d.   16 PAGES

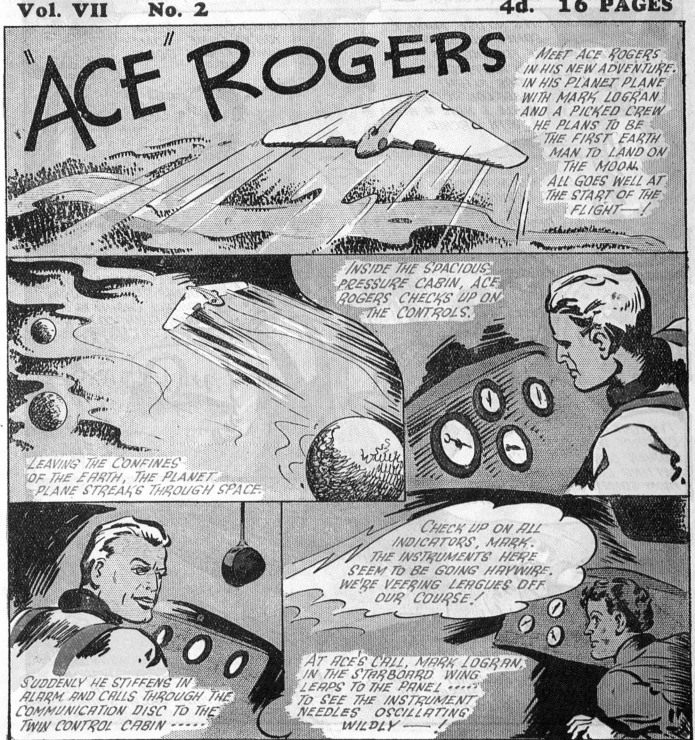

"ACE" ROGERS

MEET ACE ROGERS IN HIS NEW ADVENTURE. IN HIS PLANET PLANE WITH MARK LOGAN AND A PICKED CREW HE PLANS TO BE THE FIRST EARTH MAN TO LAND ON THE MOON. ALL GOES WELL AT THE START OF THE FLIGHT—!

INSIDE THE SPACIOUS PRESSURE CABIN, ACE ROGERS CHECKS UP ON THE CONTROLS.

LEAVING THE CONFINES OF THE EARTH, THE PLANET PLANE STREAKS THROUGH SPACE.

CHECK UP ON ALL INDICATORS, MARK. THE INSTRUMENTS HERE SEEM TO BE GOING HAYWIRE. WE'RE VEERING LEAGUES OFF OUR COURSE!

SUDDENLY HE STIFFENS IN ALARM AND CALLS THROUGH THE COMMUNICATION DISC TO THE TWIN CONTROL CABIN——

AT ACE'S CALL, MARK LOGAN, IN THE STARBOARD WING LEAPS TO THE PANEL——TO SEE THE INSTRUMENT NEEDLES OSCILLATING WILDLY——!

MARTIN POWER: SPACE INVESTIGATOR

by Mick Anglo
Power Comic **(1950)**
Martin & Reid Ltd (London)

'Power Packed Pages of Adventure and Thrills!' promised the headline of *Power Comic*, a colourful threepenny one-shot. Unfortunately the headline did not reveal that there were only eight pages of Adventures and Thrills, and that two of those were taken up with comic strips, 'Isadore Knob' and 'Charles Cole and his Magic Chalks!' There were a couple of single-page strips, 'Chuck Chance, Sheriff', and 'Police Patrol', but the lead feature, Martin Power, was given the front and back pages. It seems a lone space pirate has been looting jewel courier jets from Mars, somewhere in the vicinity of the Belt Area. 'He's flying a Martian Radarjet,' says the Chief. 'It's a tough assignment, Captain Power!' 'I'll get him, sir!' salutes the Space Investigator, adding 'It'll be tricky – a Radarjet is almost impossible to nail down with this old Rocketeer I'm flying!' Zooming over to the back page, not noticing that he has lost the yellow ink and arrived in mere red-and-blue, Power does a rapid calculation guaranteed to baffle the mind of any Martian, let alone youthful reader. 'Explosion – 8000 miles – 8 degrees X sector – 95 degrees Venus – an hour distant!' Following the pirate by Radar Magnetic Attraction, Power and the pirate fight it out on an asteroid, although how their flying fists could KO through their space helmets is unexplained. 'Well, space pirate, you'll soon be paying for your dastardly crimes!' moralises Martin Power, rocketing home.

This one-shot comic formed a companion paper to *Captain Zenith Comic*, another Mick Anglo production published by Martin & Reid. Zenith is featured in our own companion comic-book, *Super Duper Supermen!*

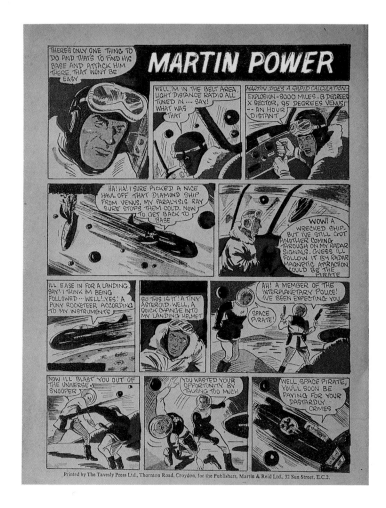

Continued on back page

SPACE HERO

(1951)
Scion Ltd (London)

'Amazing Stories of the Future!' was the headline for this sixpenny Scion Science Fiction Comic which ran for two issues in 1951. The main contributor was Norman Light, who drew the cover for No. 1, plus the adventure strips 'Galactic Patrol' and 'Commander Wade Kirkman and the Space Commandos'. The first strip started so: 'Far out in the interstellar void, many light years from their base on Mother Earth, a fighter ship of the Galactic Patrol, manned by Bradford Kane and his Mexican navigator, Carlos Lopez, are in danger of annihilation! Attacked on all sides by strike ships from the Star of Miro!' This was the strip that was boosted on the coloured cover as 'Star of Evil'. The tale begins with a battle as Brad blasts away with his Sub-atomic Beam and the aliens reply with their Electrolight Ray. 'Holy Space!' cries Brad, 'looks like the end for us!' 'You speak true, my fran' – we are in a ver' tough spot!' answers Carlos. 'Let thees peegs feel our fire power!' Scothani, head of the Miroian Army, takes the captured spacemen to see their Queen, who turns out to be a glamorous Earthlady who crashed on Miro twenty years earlier! 'My stars!' gasps Brad, while Carlos is content with 'Carramba!'

Norman Light, a newcomer to comic art and script-writing, became quite a force in the Fifties with his contributions to comic-books ranging from Miller and Scion publications, *Tit-Bits Science Fiction Comics*, and finally his own publishing house, Gould-Light Productions. The second issue of *Space Hero* was a great disappointment, featuring only one sci-fi strip, 'Don Havoc and the Mystery of the Flying Saucers'. The rest were schoolboy and funny animal strips. It contained nothing by Norman Light.

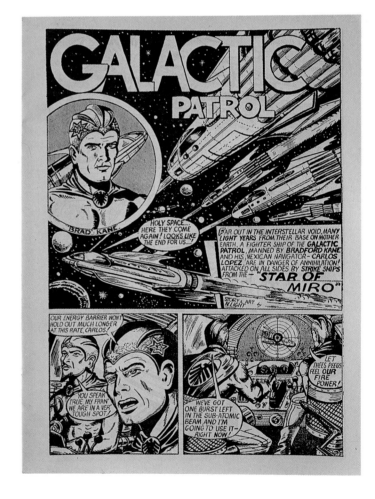

SPACE ROVER PETE

by John McCail
Dynamic Thrills **(1952)**
Gerald G. Swan Ltd (London)

'Pete, through atomic mutation, was able to endure all the extremes of heat and cold. He was also able to travel through space, his cosmic ray boosters enabling him to reach amazing speeds.' Pete's job was to investigate an immense black mass lying in outer space, a two-page task he accomplished with many an expletive: 'Gosh!', 'Wow!', 'Phew!', 'Gee!', and once, a little more suitably for a space hero, 'By Jupiter!' Rocketing to the sponge-like substance, Pete melts a way through the black stuff with his blaster. At its core he discovers a little universe. 'I think I'll land on that oval planet,' he says, but quickly regrets his decision as plants attack him, trussing him up in their creepers. Fortunately a giant stork flies down in time to peck the plant to death, but unfortunately flies Pete off to its mountain nest and feeds him to its chicks! A quick blast with his blaster and Pete is speeding across space again, 'to tell of a new world to be colonised and new dangers to be conquered'. Later longer adventures introduced Pete's uncle, a famous astronomer, and Pete's secret laboratory, where he carried out experiments in space research.

Pete's only coloured cover appearance was on the tenth and last edition of Gerald G. Swan's thirty-six-page adventure comic-book, *Dynamic Thrills*. This contained quite a lot of work by the Scottish McCail brothers, John and William. Jock's contributions also included 'Gateway to the Unknown' and a pirate yarn, 'Peril on the Main', while brother Bill's strips were 'Manders of the Met', 'Chester Kean, Detective' and 'Headline Henderson, Crime

GALLANT SCIENCE COMIC

by Ron Embleton, Terence Patrick, James Bleach
1952: Scion Ltd (London)

One of the four 'Gallant' series comic-books produced by Ron Embleton and friends for publication by Scion of Kensington High Street. An anthology of strips with the accent on the adventure rather than regular heroes, No. 2 of this comic opened with 'Past or Future' by Jim Bleach. This strip illustrated Captain Colin Davis of the Space Force in his flight to Venus, where he encountered a triceratops 'twenty times to (*sic*) big!' The second strip was 'Five Thousand Fathoms' by Terence Patrick, illustrating the historic descent into the ocean's depths by Professor Beebe and his Bathysphere. There was a serial, Chapter One of 'The Brain' entitled 'Bargain After Death', a factual strip on the invention of the aeroplane in the series 'Inventions that Have Changed the Face of the Earth', and a six-page adventure, 'Jungle of Terror'. This one, drawn by Ron Embleton, was also featured on his coloured cover and dealt with prehistoric monsters rampaging around unexplored Brazil. The centre spread, described as 'A Double Page Action Plate for Your Scrapbook', was entitled 'Battle of the Giants' and showed a struggle to the death between a tyrannosaurus and a stegosaurus as depicted by Terry Patrick.

There were three other 'Gallant' comic-books making up the series, *Gallant Western*, *Gallant Detective* and *Gallant Adventure*, and according to editor Embleton's Readers' Page, they each featured a two-page picture printed in colour. In the event, however, these appeared in regular black-and-white. Among the titles listed of forthcoming centre-spreads was 'The First Rocket to the Moon'.

GALLANT SCIENCE COMIC
Nº 2
THRILL PACKED

JUNGLE OF TERROR

ACTION 6ᴰ PACKED

"PAST OR FUTURE?" "THE BRAIN"

CAPTAIN 'SPACE' KINGLEY OF THE INTERPLANETARY RANGERS

by R.W. Jobson (artist) Ray Sonin (writer)
(1952) Sampson Low Marston & Co (London)

'Fly into tomorrow with Captain Robert "Space" Kingley of the Interplanetary Rangers!' invited the blurb of the first hardback annual, *The Adventures of Captain 'Space' Kingley*. Chapter One, enticingly entitled 'Introducing a Hero', began: 'The gyro-jet blasted its way across the summer sky, hovered high over the domes of the World University Centre, and gently dropped to earth on the jet-blackened parking-drome that surrounded the expanse of white buildings. Captain Robert "Space" Kingley, Senior Field Officer of the Interplanetary Rangers, flicked off the controls, stretched his long legs, and lifted a hand to straighten his sky-blue uniform.' A new space hero had arrived, this time one who had not got his own regular comic-book as a pictorial vehicle for his exploits. But he had got a sidekick: Shorty Rowe, 'his batman, housekeeper, assistant, handyman, and Number One admirer.' 'It's a h'onour, guv'nor,' said Shorty, referring to the headlines in that day's issue of *World Tidings*: 'Ace Ranger Voted Man of the Year by World Faculty of Junior Scientists'. Soon 'the life-like colour of television enabled millions to recognise the medals on Space's chest: the Red Order of Mars, the Moon Medal (struck to celebrate the opening of regular traffic to the satellite), the Venus Exploration Star and the World Service Cross, battle honours in man's scientific and bloodless conquest of nature.' The book contains six missions, beginning with 'The Creeping Death' and concluding with 'The Submarine City', but it would be the next volume, *Space Kingley and the Secret Squadron*, which brought the hero bang into the world of comics. Twenty-four pages of this eighty-page book were depicted in strips: 'Operation Ocean', 'Bottled Beetles' and 'Target Earth'. Kingley had a new backup team: Yu-ten, the inscrutable man from the East, Taffy Jones, the fiery Welshman, Bats Cholmondeley, 'effete outside, steel within,' and stolid Chatty Olsen. In their combined hands lay the fate of the world.

R.W. Jobson, a name unknown in mainline comic-books, proved expert at both wash and full-colour work in this series, later adding strip cartoons that moved Space Kingley closer to the *Eagle*'s Dan Dare.

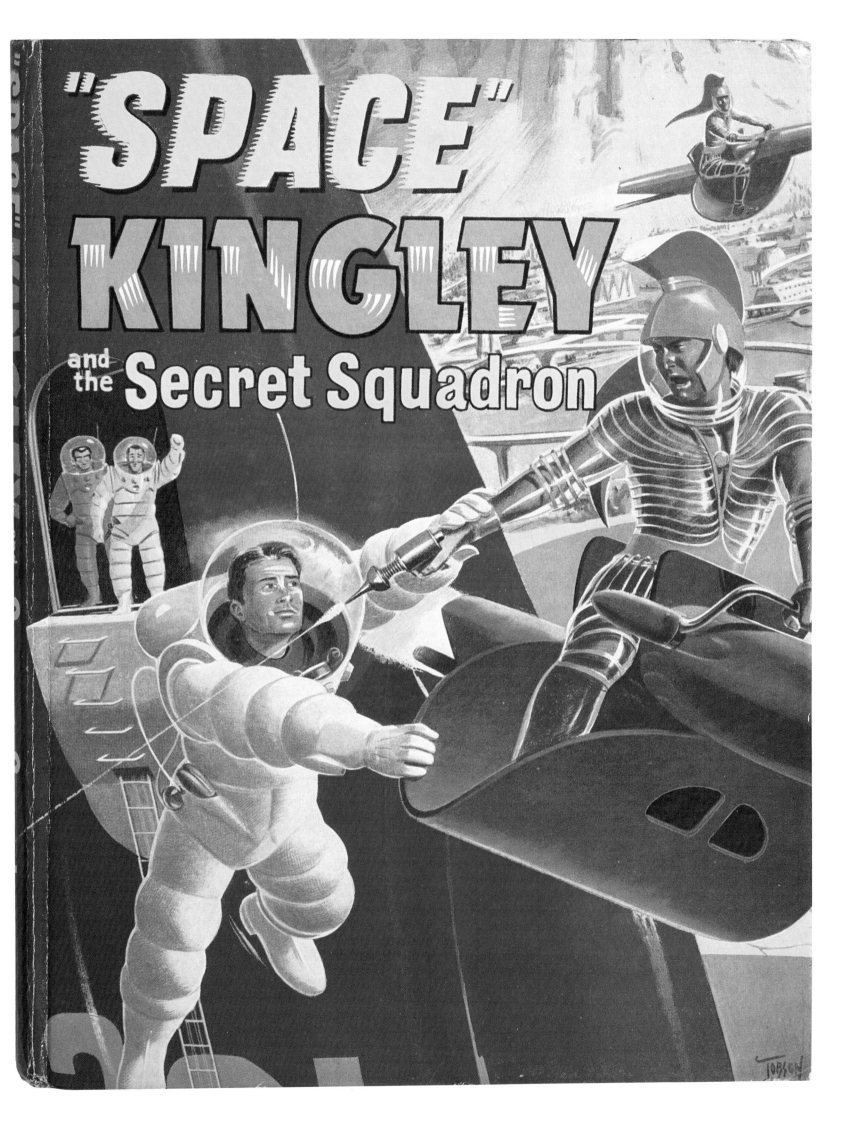

SPACE ACE:
SPACE SQUADRON COMMANDER

Lone Star Magazine (1953)
DCMT Ltd (Palmers Green)

Space Ace made his debut as Ace Hart in No. 1 of *Lone Star Magazine*, a bumper fourpenny-worth issued in March 1953 by Die Cast Metal Toys to tie in with their products. Unfortunately, editor Fred Phillips had not heard of 'Ace Hart the Atom Man', star of *Superthriller* comic since 1948. Foldes Press, the publishers, dropped him a line, and from No. 3 of *Lone Star*, Ace Hart was renamed Space Ace. 'Journey to Zimbolus' was the opening episode, with the spaceship LS1 (Lone Star One, get it ?) roaring off from Gopher Gulch, Texas on 27 May 1969 – sixteen years into the future. Ace Hart, Sheriff of Tarrant County (where the comic's editor was apparently his deputy) was knocked unconscious during the pursuance of his duties by a small meteorite. This rendered him immune to all radioactivity, and coupling this with his previous career as a stratosphere pilot and amateur scientist, it made him the ideal person to captain Professor McKay's new spaceship. The crew consisted of McKay, Chief Pilot Bill Haines, Dr Wang Fu the physicist, Silas Granger, mining expert, Monty Milne ('Oh, I say, dash it!'), and Marmaduke the Monkey.

The artist who drew the early adventures of Ace Hart/Space Ace remained anonymous, but the series was shortly to be taken over by the redoubtable Ron Turner, a true sci-fi stylist. *Lone Star* ran for over 100 issues, and was originated as a vehicle to promote DCMT's linked line of toys, most of which featured 'Steve Larrabee the Lone Star Rider' and his weaponry. Space Ace's rayguns were also a top seller of the period.

ACE HART
SPACE SQUADRON COMMANDER

BILL HAINES
(CHIEF PILOT)

DR. WANG FU
(PHYSICIST)

MARMADUKE

SILAS GRANGER
(MINING EXPERT)

PROFESSOR McKAY

MONTY MILNE

TEXAS ... MAY 13, 1969.

After a running fight with hold-up men, Ace Hart, Sheriff of Tarrant County, Texas; ex-stratosphere pilot, and amateur experimental scientist is caught a glancing blow by a small meteorite and knocked unconscious. As he falls his body rolls on to the meteorite. Unknown to Ace Hart, the meteoric contains a minute particle of a mineral in the uranium group but many, many times more powerful. In his unconscious state Ace's body is impregnated with the rays of the rare one, and because his blood group is an extremely rare one, he suffer no ill-effects ... in fact, he actually becomes entirely immune to all radio-activity...

Whilst Ace is lying unconscious, a much larger meteorite falls a few miles away close to the Anglo-American Interplanetary Research Station at Gopher Gulch. The scientists who note its fall, discover it contains a variety of uranium of greater power than any found on earth which they name No.39, and prove that it can be used to power the Space Ship "L S 1" they have built many millions of miles without refuelling. The scientists soon find, through their solar-midanium telescopes and planetracecometers that the meteor could have come only from the planet Zimbolus. Hasty conferences are called and it is decided to send the "L S 1" to Zimbolus and set up a factory to mine and refine the mineral ...

TEXAS ... MAY 17, 1969 ...

Two weeks after Ace Hart was struck by the meteorite, his body is found and carried to the Research Station Hospital where he is brought round. Fully recovered, he is taken to Professor McKay who is astounded at the behaviour of a geiger counter that is in the laboratory where he is chatting to Ace. Many tests are made and it is then that they discover Ace's immunity to radio-activity. McKay immediately asks him to travel on "L S 1" to Zimbolus and is more than gratified to learn about his experience as a pilot and his scientific knowledge as well as his experience as a rancher, for they intend to take farm stock as well as other animals, and seed for food and observation as there is good reason to believe that the atmosphere and climate may be suitable. Also, observation of the planet over long periods has led the scientists to believe that if it contains human life then its people probably live in large, natural caves which seem to be roofed with some kind of opaque mineral which filters the sun's rays and by reflection and refraction acts as a highly controlled heating system.

The story opens with Space Ship "L S 1" being loaded preparatory to the take-off.

NOW READ ON

SPACE ACE: GUARDIAN OF THE UNIVERSE

by Ron Turner
Space Ace **(1960)**
Atlas Publishing & Distributing Co (London)

'The Barrier' was the opening episode of Space Ace when he was promoted to his own monthly comic-book by his new publisher, Atlas. 'Returning from an outer space mission, Space Ace and Sergeant Bill Crag enter what appears to be a harmless cloud of cosmic dust, but…' Several things have happened to our hero since his *Lone Star* days. The original gang of seven have been reduced to two, Ace and military-moustached NCO, Sergeant Bill. From his early days as Space Squadron Commander, Ace has been promoted to the Guardian of the Universe, and certainly his delineation has improved beyond all expected bounds, thanks to the brilliant brushwork of Ron Turner. The language is livelier, too: 'Flaming jets!' swears Sgt Bill, while Ace riposts with the milder 'By Jupiter!' By the time *Space Ace* reached its allotted span of thirty-three editions, our hero was being drawn by a skilled Spanish artist, José M. Bea, who regularly drew the coloured covers.

Among the rarest collectables from the Sixties are the lapel badges and identification cards for the Space Ace Cadets, a club which cost but one shilling (five pence) and a clipped coupon to join. 'Enlisted Cadets will also have the Secret Space Ace Code revealed to them, and will be able to decipher a Secret Message from Space Ace that will in future appear in every issue of *Space Ace Comic*.' The first such appeared in No. 2, and began : 'FRQP DSFPV BANLR NFT…'

THE JET COMIC

(1953)
Hamilton & Co (London)

'Jack Trent, Space Flyer' was the leading feature in this twenty-eight page sixpenny comic-book published by the science-fiction specialists, Hamilton & Co, Trent, drawn anonymously, and based closely on 'Dan Dare, Pilot of the Future', the front-page star of the current best-selling comic, *Eagle*. Trent is the pilot of 'The Starflash', a spaceship designed by Professor Fordyce to make an exploratory voyage to the moons of Saturn. The crew consists of the prof's daughter Carla, a radio-physicist, and Don Porter, mechanic. 'Jumping snakes!' cries Jack, spotting a Flying Saucer. He dons his Crystophane Space-rompers and propels himself by mini-jet to the Saucer, which is damaged. Inside lies a mummified Martian, Donaz. They revive him. 'Mazwor ungwi zawroy!' he says, until they put his head into a thought-transfer machine which enables them to understand Martian language. It is the start of a nine-page epic, which ends happily with a return to Earth and mechanic Don murmuring, 'Lumme! Now for some fish and chips!'

Jet Comic also introduced Ron Embleton's latest super-hero creation, 'Captain Atom'. This is Mike Halliday who dons Professor Helmut Dakar's atomic helmet and is transformed into 'a mighty figure of strength!' There is also a Tarzan-type hero, 'Mogog the Mighty', and 'Space Survey' starring Rocky Granite, Stubby Phips, Bruno Spaatz, Rene Morrain, and her father, the Professor. He invented the rocketship that takes them to the planet Skorda, where only men may live. Can Rocky save Rene from 'the shapeless slimy creature rising from the deep?' 'Will they manage to make the craft spaceworthy and get back to Earth?' We shall never know: *Jet Comic* failed to make a second issue.

Jet Comic was published by Hamilton's, the firm who were having great success with their monthly pocket-sized magazine, *Authentic Science Fiction*. No. 41 was advertised on the back cover. Unfortunately, although succeeding issues of *Jet* were planned, it failed to attract sufficient readership to warrant even a No. 2.

THE JET COMIC

6D

THE "STARFLASH" — A SPACESHIP DESIGNED BY PROFESSOR FORDYCE, IS MAKING A VOYAGE TO EXPLORE THE MOONS OF SATURN... BESIDES THE PROFESSOR, THE SHIP HAS AS CREW — JACK TRENT, PILOT; CARLA, THE PROFESSOR'S DAUGHTER, WHO IS A RADIO-PHYSICIST, AND DON PORTER, A MECHANIC — THE SHIP HAS BEEN DRIVING THROUGH SPACE FOR MANY DAYS AND THE CREW ARE LOOKING FORWARD TO LANDING ON THE SATELLITE TITAN WHEN, SUDDENLY THE RADASCOPE SHOWS AN OBJECT WHERE ONLY EMPTY SPACE SHOULD BE ——————

JACK TRENT SPACE FLYER

DICK BARTON: SPECIAL AGENT

Comet (1953)
Amalgamated Press Ltd (London)

'Dick Barton – Special Agent!' snapped the announcer, and in blasted the signature tune – 'Dum-dum-diddle-iddle-dum-dum...' It was heard every weeknight plus an omnibus edition on Saturdays on the BBC Light Programme, starting on 7 October 1946 and ending on 30 March 1951. Captain Barton, ex-Commando, with his tight little team of Jock the Scot and Snowy the cockney, versus the greatest criminal masterminds of all time: a natural for a comic strip hero. Unfortunately his weekly strip adventures did not begin until two years after the radio serial had gasped its last gasp! But when he did start, he was both updated and downgraded. Dick leaped into tomorrow with 'The Flying Saucer Mystery', but was reduced from two assistants to one, Snowy White – and Snowy was reduced, too: in age. He became another of those typical teenage sidekicks, popular in the comic world since the Victorian day of Sexton Blake and Tinker. In this serial, Dick became the first man in the Moon, and Snowy the first teenager. Paced out at three breathless pages a week, it was the lead strip in *Comet*, with Dick and Snowy zapping it out with Count Phansigar and his evil Space Commandos. 'Thunder and lightning!' swore the Count.

Comet, a popular tabloid twopenny comic which the Amalgamated Press took over from Cheshire publisher J.B. Allen, underwent several changes of format during its thirteen-year lifetime. From 29 March 1952 it suddenly shrank into a twenty-page comic-book, reflecting the upswing in popularity of the American format.

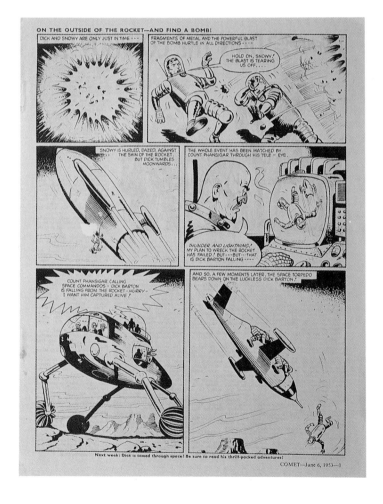

DICK BARTON

and the

FLYING SAUCER MYSTERY!

COMET

EVERY MONDAY 3D

No. 255.
June 6, 1953

THE BRITISH ROCKET HAS REACHED THE MOON! ITS ROCKETS BLASTING AT ONE TENTH POWER, IT IS SETTLING SLOWLY DOWN, TAIL FIRST, TOWARDS THE MOON'S CRAGGY SURFACE.
BUT UNKNOWN TO THE MEN INSIDE - TWO OF COUNT PHANSIGAR'S SPACE COMMANDOS ARE WALKING LIKE FLIES ON THE OUTSIDE OF THE HUGE STEEL ROCKET.

THEIR MAGNETIC BOOTS HOLD THEM SECURE -- AS THEY ANCHOR A TIME-BOMB TO MAKE THE BRITISH ROCKET CRASH --

THE BOMB IS SET TO EXPLODE IN FIVE MINUTES - WE MUST HURRY AWAY!

BUT INSIDE THE ROCKET, DICK BARTON HEARS THE SCRAPE OF THEIR STEEL BOOTS.

SIR JOHN! SOMETHING - OR SOMEONE - IS MOVING ABOUT ON THE OUTSIDE OF THE ROCKET! I CAN HEAR THEM!

(Continued on next page)

STAR-ROCKET: THE COMIC OF THE FUTURE

(1953)
Comyns Ltd (London)

Ron Embleton, fast becoming a past master at sci-fi, drew two of the three strips that made up No. 1 of *Star-Rocket*, 'The Robot' and the somewhat dubiously titled 'They Came From Uranus'. The former starred Jason, the Greatest of All Men, a blond bronzed argonaut of tomorrow. 'On Earth, man enjoys peace and happiness. The perfect world, forged by his forefathers in blood and toil for over thirty centuries, is his. Wars and hatred have long been forgotten – men have forgotten the meaning of the words, for this is 4000 AD.' Into this paradise zooms Radok, an evil scientist banished from Venus. He lands in the Himalayas and sets up a superlab, cackling the while: 'Enjoy yourselves while you can, Earthmen – *he-he!* – for tomorrow you will have your first taste of terror for a thousand years!' Radok dispatches his giant robot to destroy mankind, but reckons without Jason. 'One man armed with a mirror as a shield could defy the robot and its ray! I, Jason, shall be that man!' And he is!

The run of five issues of *Star-Rocket* comprise a very special set of sci-fi strips of the Fifties. Each comic-book varies from the last, No. 3 being especially interesting as the entire twenty-page issue, including cover, is by Ron Turner. Embleton returns in No. 4 with another 'Jason' saga, and another hero who appears twice is 'Paul Raynor, Space Pioneer'.

CAPTAIN SCIENTO

by Ron Turner
***Star-Rocket* (1953)** *All Action Comic*
Comyns Ltd (London) Alexander Moring (London)

Captain Sciento, wearing a natty beard and moustache, is sent on a mission by the United Interplanetary Organisation. Also aboard the rocket ship 'Asteroid' is Sciento's daughter, Stella, acting as his second pilot. 'If the UIO knew I'd brought you, I'd get sacked,' he says. 'But what can a man do with a brat like you?' 'Nuts!' is Stella's short reply. They arrive at Venus and see a strange ship. 'Flaring rockets! What in the name of Pete is that?' cries Stella. 'Looks like one of those flying saucers they discovered back in 1950!' answers her dad. Soon they are captives of Varon, Future Ruler of the Solar System – he claims. 'Sneer, Earthman – but the time is near when all the Solar System will bow before me and my followers!' Varon's method is a vast Solar Condenser which will concentrate the sun's rays upon Earth with a 'frying tonight' effect. 'Giegen mikton salsar voros sur extor sen doros!' he adds, which is parenthetically translated as 'Take these two away and exterminate them!' But with the aid of the Venusian Forces of Peace, Sciento is able to wind up the spectacular proceedings with 'Good old Mother Earth, saved again!'

Originally published in *Star-Rocket*, Sciento was later reprinted in one of Alexander Moring's bumper shilling comic-books, *All Action*. This was given the luxury of a full colour cover by Ron Turner, which set the strip in July 2050. Turner's original style of heavily brushworked illustration had now reached a peak, after his tentative beginnings in the Scion *Big Comic* series of five years earlier.

CAPTAIN VALIANT: ACE OF THE INTERPLANETARY PATROL

by Mick Anglo
Space Comics **(1953)**
Arnold Book Company (Edgware)

'Top Secret!' screamed the crimson panel on the cover of the first issue (No. 50) of *Space Comics*. 'Now it can be told! Sleek space freighters already streak the skies between Earth and the planets. Policing the skies are the super-jets of Captain Vic Valiant's Interplanetary Police Patrol. The exploits of Captain Valiant, tough veteran of space travel and hero of campaigns on Mars, Luro and Reus, are known throughout the galaxies, but now, at last, we are privileged to reveal them to you, our Earth readers, for the first time! Friends! We bring you – Outpost on the Moon!' Inside there was more essential information. The Reussis, it seemed, had been defeated by the United Forces of the Interplanetary Command, but due to the vast distances involved, space raiders from Reus were soon attacking neighbouring planets again. It was up to the IPP, which meant, of course, Vic Valiant. Using an oxygen pellet so that he didn't need to don his plastic vacuum helmet, Vic speeds via auto-flying belt to Lunar outpost 723. He is set upon by Reussis, crying 'Tegi e poce evila!', which is translated via a handy asterisk as 'Take the patrolman alive!' Valiant fights back: 'Come on, you Reussi carrion! Sample the paralysing effect of my electro-space stiletto!', but is soon overpowered. Captive of the Reussi chief Falstar, he is taken to Reus aboard the hyper-space ship 'Carona' where he is forced to fight an underwater battle with an Octocuda. Seventeen pages later all ends well – until the next adventure, of course.

The motto of the IPP was 'Forward to the Future', and this was the headline to the *Interplanetary Police Gazette*, the official organ of the IPP, written (by spacemail) by Captain Vic Valiant, who greeted his readers with 'Hello, Space Cadets!' This mock newspaper announced that the latest Hon. Mem. of the IPP was none other than the internationally famous cowboy star, Tex Ritter! There was no such Hon. Membership for his horse, White Flash.

PETE MANGAN:
OF THE SPACE PATROL

by King-Ganteaume
Pete Mangan **(1953)**
L. Miller & Son (London)

'With the dropping of the Atomic Bomb, other more advanced planets began to take an interest in the world, deeming that now our Earth is advancing into a stage of civilisation worthy of their notice. By 3490 AD Earth has been permitted to join the Planet Federation for defence against the space outlaws who lurk ready to pounce on peaceful interplanetary ships.' In possibly the farthest flung, futuristically speaking, series of sci-fi strips, Pete Mangan stars heroically, sometimes solo, sometimes as part of a team. Although the title billed him 'of the Space Patrol', Pete's inside adventures vary from 'of the Planet Patrol' to 'of the International Space Patrol'. Pete's team, when it appears, consists of Commander Joe on the video, Commander Ted and Commander Bill. These three are replaced by a blonde known only as Sweetheart in Pete's second adventure, but as she turns out to be in the pay of the Corsairs from Klangor, she probably doesn't count. In that episode, by the way, Pete is addressed as Patrolman, and he operates out of the Central City of Metropol. But why try to sort out the confusion when there are such strange scenes as Pete dangling from a pirate spaceship ('The spacers nudge into the black blotch of Nova Klangor that lifts and parts at their approach'), popping into the Asteroid Club, ('with trembling fingers he gulps down a goblet of harsh Klangorian liquor'), and watching a dancing girl gyrate ('Vilma looks frightened as with brilliance she dances the Dance of Death')?

Peter Mangan and his supporting shorts – 'Rip Clark', 'Hooty the Tec', etc – were packaged by the independent comic company, King-Ganteaume Productions, who produced a number of comic-books for L. Miller, Scion and other small publishers. Ganteaume was said to be a French-Canadian ex-soldier who set up the outfit on his war gratuity.

A BRITISH PRODUCTION
PUBLISHED BY
L. MILLER
& SON Ltd.
LONDON.

Pete Mangan

Nº 55 6ᴰ

OF THE SPACE PATROL

SPACE COMMANDER KERRY

by Mick Anglo
Space Commander Kerry **(1953)**
L. Miller & Son Ltd (London)

Steve Kerry was Space Commander in the Interplanetary Special Service, and his two lieutenants were Rick Shaw and Tubby Low. The first adventure of this intrepid trio, 'The Atmoscope Mystery', saw them heading for Planet Mica in search of Professor Zeink's missing machine. 'The Atmoscope is a special sphere set to rotate round a planet that has no atmosphere such as will support life such as we know it,' explained the Prof. 'Domed cities will be a thing of the past.' As Steve Kerry answered – 'Uh-huh!' He was wittier once they started on their flight to Mica. 'This should get rid of some of your surplus blubber, Tubby!' he chaffed, and the obese one riposted with, 'Bah! You're just jealous of my muscles!' Commander Kerry also had a few futuristic expletives of his own. 'Space alive!' he cried, and once, 'By the sacred Biduls of Venus!' With the aid of action-suits and persona-jets they are able to foil a Medissi plot to use the Atmoscope, boosting its electro-magnetism with cosmic rays to use its power-ramp to shower the Earth with hordes of meteorites. At the back of the comic, the *Interplanetary News Report*, Official Organ of the ISS, solicited readers' letters, plugged companion comics, and issued Special Messages. The first was: 'All ISS spacecraft will keep clear of Hyper Spaceway Z23-B194, in vicinity of Lurgo and between Reus and Ferro, until further notice. Interplanetary police patrols are patrolling this area while operations against Reussi raiders are being extended to Reussi satellites.' Something to remember whilst scootering to school.

Editor and writer Mick Anglo had served in the Special Boat Service during World War Two, and enjoyed creating futuristic forces on similar lines. The ISS uniform was explained in detail, from Ultra Violet Radar Goggles and Contra-Gravity Automatic Flying Belt, down to the Volta Hand-gun operating on deadly Pressure Flash or temporary Paralysis Ray.

SPACE COMMANDER

KERRY

No 50

6d

The ATMOSCOPE MYSTERY and OTHER FEATURES

SPARKY MALONE: SPACE COMMANDO

by Mick Anglo
***Space Commando Comics* (1953)**
L. Miller & Son Ltd (London)

'Thrilling Adventures in Deep Space and Beyond!' promised the bannerline of *Space Commando Comics*, which starred Space Commodore Sparky Malone, 'the fearless, tough leader of the Spacial Assignment Group'. His first published case, 'Operation Hostage', began with a meeting with the Supreme Military Commander of the United Planets. It seemed Professor Western, eminent atomic scientist, had been captured by Axis forces who were holding him captive at Truyk. But perhaps a word of background information would not go amiss: 'War rages between the peace-loving planets of Earth, Mars and Jupiter, known as the United Planets, and the evil forces of Venus, Karoc, Mercury and Gor, known as the Axis. The actions are fought in space and on the lesser planets, but raids are carried out on the main planets by small shock forces' – enter the Space Commandos. Leaving his Lieutenant, Jerry Bernstein, behind the lines, Sparky flies over via his Self-propellant, or Flying Belt. Unfortunately he is nabbed by a guard: 'Push ub da hands, twick!' A charge from Sparky's temporary paralysis gun and the prof is soon saved, while the enemy post is exploded with a *Crump!* 'Neat! Yes indeed!' says Sparky. At the end of the comic there appears the *Interplanetary Group Report*, Official Organ of the Special Assignments Group, complete with Editor's Letter by Spacemail bringing Greetings from All Planets! Apart from plugs for other Miller comics, there is news that Freddie Randall, famous bandleader of Radio, Stage and TV, has made a beautiful model spaceship of his own design!

Editor Mick Anglo, working from his own Gower Studios, included information sheets on Spacecraft Recognition and SC uniforms. The latter included Heavy Anti-Flash Battle Gauntlets, an Anti-Radioactivity Cape, a Volta Hand Gun, and Shatter Grenades carried in Pouch Pockets.

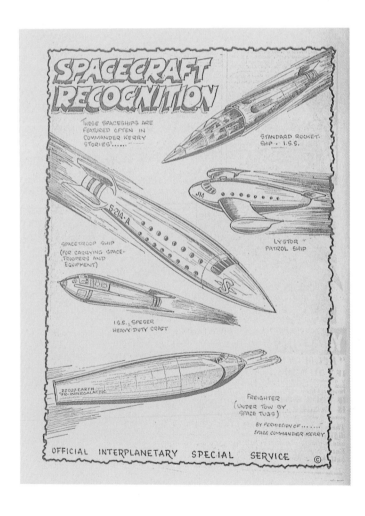

HAL STARR

by Sidney Jordan
***Strange Worlds, Super Sonic* (1953)**
Man's World Comics Ltd (Surrey)

*S*trange Worlds ('Thrills with the Unknown!') was a double-feature comic-book. Top hero was Hal Starr, Ace Investigator for the Galactic Federation's Space Security Patrol. Hal's debut adventure was 'Space Horror', in which Hal and his partner, Les, go beyond the planet Pluto in search of a missing cargo ship, 'Nostradamus'. They locate the vessel blown asunder and adrift for ever in the airless void, 'a sight to daunt even the stoutest heart!' Crying 'Great Space!', Hal and Les encounter Flying Saucers and floating octopoids before rescuing the survivors from a fate worse than a drop in pressure. Hal Starr was one of the few British heroes to be syndicated to Australian comic-books. Backing Hal was a secondary series called 'Discoveries Incorporated', which featured Professor Graham FGS and Jim Gilbert, MI Mech. E., plus the prof's nephew, sixteen-year-old Don. Discoveries Inc is 'a combination of science, technical knowledge, and red-blooded adventure', as may be surmised from the title of their first adventure, 'Abominable Snowmen'.

Man's World Comics was a division of the Body Sculpture Club, who operated from the Manor House, Worcester Park, Surrey. Their back covers were packed with Big Bargains, including 'Look Bronzed Tarzan with Sun Tan Plus' for 7s 6d, and 'The Body Sculpture Muscle Weaver', nine outfits in one for 7s 6d, and 'Wear the Body Sculpture Tie – Be Recognised as a Man of Strength!', boys' size 5s. Hal Starr's creator, Sidney Jordan, would shortly originate the briliant sci-fi newspaper strip, 'Jeff Hawke – Spacerider', which ran for many years in the *Daily Express*.

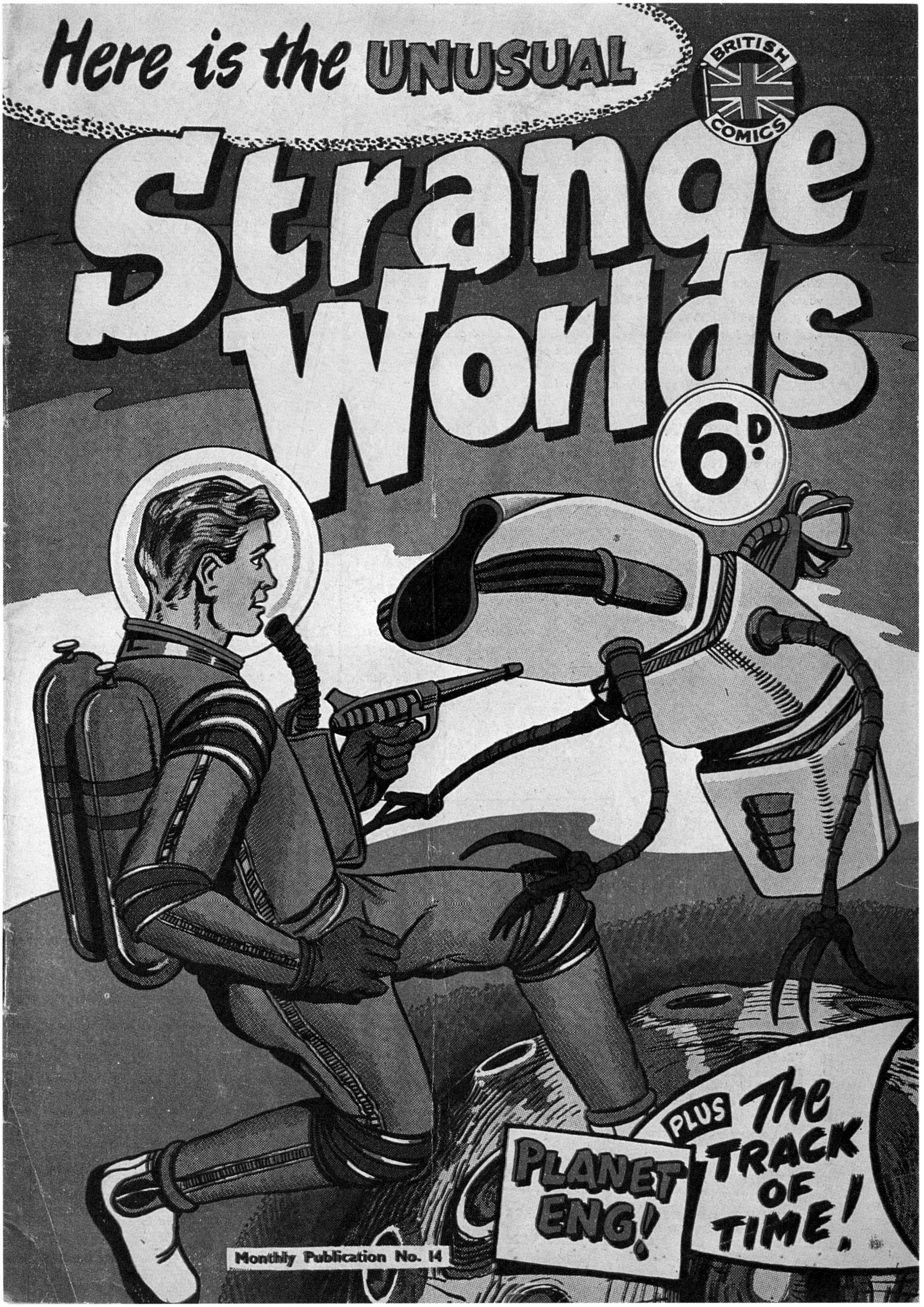

Here is the UNUSUAL
BRITISH COMICS
Strange Worlds
6D.
PLUS The TRACK OF TIME!
PLANET ENG!
Monthly Publication No. 14

JOURNEY INTO SPACE!

True Life Adventures (1953)
Man's World Comics Ltd (Surrey)

This monthly comic-book had one issue of special interest to sci-fi fans, No. 13. 'Journey Into Space' was the title of the famous radio serial by Charles Chilton, and this was used as the headline and the title of the lead strip by this comic. There the resemblance ended, for this was a semi-authentic illustrated history of man's attempts at space-flight. The cover depicted the curious means of transport employed, the Stratoloon! The strip's preamble set the scene: 'The first amazing pioneer flights into the stratosphere by Professor Auguste Piccard in 1931 led to this thrilling story of an American expedition when three scientists had a miraculous escape from twelve miles up.' A teacher tells his pupils, 'Such a journey into the great unknown was breath-taking!', and the pictures take over the story of Piccard, who went ten miles straight up and then was eventually found by mountain guides, safe and sound on a glacier. That was May 1931; on 18 August the following year he was up again, taking photographs. Then in 1934, 28 July, five Americans in a Stratoloon, six times the size of Piccard's, surged skyward. 'In the half light the aluminium gondola looks grotesque, like some diabolical space-mine! It has three manholes fitted with quick-release covers and clamps, a dozen portholes in the globe, and three appendices to reduce the risk of a burst!' But all does not go well. 'Cripes, cap'n! Look!!! The envelope's tearing!' The slashing fabric produces frictional electricity and the gas ignites, the balloon explodes, hurtling towards Earth. Finally their parachute opens and they plunge into the sea, the altitude record broken and the way into space established. As the schoolteacher says, 'A true life adventure stranger than fiction!'

True Life Adventures carried the usual Man's World Guarantee: 'All Man's World Comics contain only clean, thrilling adventure stories and are warranted to maintain the highest standard of healthy entertainment.' If only their standard of artwork had been equally guaranteed.

JOURNEY INTO SPACE!

BRITISH COMICS

True Life Adventures

6D

also inside...
PIRATE
GOLD
...
DAREDEVILS
OVER
NIAGARA
THRILLS! CHILLS! SPILLS!

Monthly Publication No. 12

CAPTAIN FUTURE

by Norman Light
***Spaceman* (1935)** *Outer Space*
Gould-Light Company (London) George Turton (London)

Spaceman, boldly subtitled 'Comic of the Future', was the first personal publication by artist-writer Norman Light. Captain Future, his hero, was introduced with an informative preamble. 'In the year 1986, man at last broke the chains that bound him to the Earth! The first rocket made a successful landing on the Moon, and interplanetary travel had begun. Within twenty years, Lunar Station on the Moon had developed into a huge space port, with large cities to house the crew and officials! With the discovery of a new fuel known as Protonite, spaceships were soon blasting the star trails to Mars, Jupiter, Venus and Mercury! But even in the void of space, lawlessness, robbery and violence were not uncommon! The year of 2020 AD saw the formation of a Galactic Police Force known as the Star Rovers Patrol!' And that is where the story really starts. 'From out of interstella (*sic*) void came a startling appeal, a cry for help in a strange galactic language! Hurtling to answer this mysterious call is that interplanetary crusader, Captain Future, in "The Masters of Xanthi!" Suddenly his long range telepath begins to buzz.' The message reads, 'Zac su nerim! Zfft itz! Zarling yat!' Small wonder Cap Future cries, 'Holy space!' His electronic translator device comes in handy: 'Help! This is a ship of the Krishna Republic, position sector 1534, ten parsecs out past Saturn! We are being attacked!' Switching to overdrive, Cap zooms the twenty light-years gap in moments, thwarting General Glav and his Croms with his multi-projection trick that makes his lone ship look like a whole fleet. Later in the comic, Cap stars again in an opera entitled 'Bandits from the Asteroid Hideout', which introduces the lovely Eldra from Uranus.

Norman Light, a productive and well-liked newcomer to strip illustration, quickly expanded his activities from drawing for Mick Anglo's comic-books to publishing his own. His jam-packed artwork gave great value for sixpence, and apart from sci-fi strips he drew the excellent cowboy monthly, *Ace-High Western Comic*.

THOR STEEL: CHIEF OF THE INTERPLANETARY POLICE

Super-Sonic the Super Comic (1953)
Sports Cartoons Ltd (Surrey)

Thor Steel, 'Spaceman Extraordinary', was the leading light of *Super-Sonic the Super Comic*, a monthly book which started from No. 13. The introduction read: 'The year, 2210 AD. Thor Steel is a famous scientist-cum-adventurer who rips aside the veil of mystery that surrounds the hidden galaxies of deep space. He is also Chief of the Interplanetary Scientific Security Police Force', or ISSPF for short. In his first adventure, 'Flaming Peril', Thor is assisted by Gurwen Selim, a Martian explorer. Gurwen is four feet tall, has three eyes and four arms, two of which are telescopic and retract into his sides. His hands bear suction pads instead of fingers. Otherwise Gurwen is pretty normal. The team is exploring deep space when they encounter an old enemy, Captain Greg Weston, piloting a pirate craft smuggling Ansumin drugs to Planet RX. The dustup that ensues is nothing compared with Thor's second adventure, 'Space War', in which he meets Kanta, Mad Dictator of Planet R4 who dreams of conquering the Universe.

Hal Starr of the Space Security Patrol made a guest appearance in the first issue of *Super-Sonic*, in the adventure entitled 'The Invaders'. *Super-Sonic* was one of a batch of monthly comic-books published by Sports Cartoons, a division of the Body Sculpture Club of Worcester Park, distributing through L. Miller & Son. The editor was Jim Lee, with Jim Gilbert as art editor. It bore the legend: 'One of the series of Sports Cartoons Books written by British authors, illustrated by British artists, designed for British readers.'

NEW! TERRIFIC!

SUPER- SONIC

6D

The SUPER COMIC

A SPORTS CARTOON BOOK

BRITISH THROUGHOUT

INSIDE :: "FLAMING PERIL" AND - "The Invaders"!

Monthly Publication No. 13

SPACE SCOUTS

by Ron Turner
***Laurie's Space Annual* (1953)**
T. Werner Laurie (London)

'Death of a Planet!' was the title of the eight-page two-colour sci-fi strip that saved *Laurie's Space Annual* from being a total disaster. This stylish Ron Turner story once again shows the artist's mastery of the brush, standing out against the scratchy stuff that fills the rest of this cheapo production. Turner sets his tale in the year 2050. 'Since the advent of space travel in the year 1995, the Scout movement has expanded to embrace the other planets. Three Space Scouts, John Carter, Joe Sellers and Tubby Levis, with their Scoutmaster Bill Craig, are on their way to the first Venusian Jamboree.' Suddenly big Bill gives a cry, 'Jumping Jupiter!' as a space cruiser of vast dimensions draws their small ship, 'The Arrow', into its depths. 'Don't panic, boys!' advises Bill. 'Remember – Be Prepared!' The Scouts are taken to Voran, ruler of planet Zethana, who plans to take over the Earth by wiping out its population! He reckons without the Space Scouts, and soon Bill and his boys are escaping by gyro-car, racing into space and blowing up the entire planet with hydro-atomic bombs. 'Rough justice, sir!' says a Scout. 'Rough justice but poetic justice,' says Bill. 'Destroyed by the weapons with which they planned to destroy us.' And it is off to the Jamboree!

This 'colourful annual for all space-minded youngsters' promised much, and indeed its contributors included John Kier Cross and Sydney J. Bounds, notable names in sci-fi. But colourful cover (by Terry Maloney) and Ron Turner's strip apart, it was a disappointment, especially for the asking price of seven shillings and sixpence (37½ pence).

LAURIE'S SPACE ANNUAL

TOBOR THE GREAT

by James Bleach
Star Comic **(1954)**
Donald F. Peters (London)

'This is a story of the future – a story that might take place tomorrow! *Star Comic* exclusively presents the exciting picture-strip version of Republic Pictures' science-fiction film, *Tobor the Great!*' This popular picture appeared in a five-page feature as the lead strip for No. 1 of a new monthly comic-book issued by Donald F. Peters in his series of DP – Dependable Publications, which were distibuted by L. Miller & Son. Edited by myself, the concept was the first 'Showbiz' comic, embracing stars from all the media – films, television, radio, records and even Wild West carnivals (Cal McCord and his horse, Ladybird)! Tobor the Great was a robot designed to take the place of humans on the first space flight. Unfortunately his inventor, Professor Nordstrom (Taylor Holmes) reckoned without saboteurs. Tobor himself visited Britain on a publicity tour of those cinemas showing the film.

Packed in *Star Comic*'s twenty pages were comic strips starring Bob Monkhouse, 'TV's Top Tickler', who at the time was starring on BBC Television in *Fast and Loose*; Jill Day, 'She's Sunny and Gay'; Eric Morecambe and Ernie Wise from radio's *You're Only Young Once*, and Cal McCord 'Along the Pecos Trail'.

Today the comic stands as an unusual souvenir of yesterday's showbiz. Unhappily it was not a success and closed after its second edition.

REX STRONG: SPACE ACE

by Nat Brand
***Space Story Omnibus* (1955) *Giant Book of Amazing Stories,
Whopper Space Stories***
Collins Children's Press (Glasgow)

Set in an unspecified future, Rex Strong is discovered in his laboratory poring over the blueprint of his new spaceship when an intruder stuns him with a ray-gun. By the time he revives, the mysterious assailant has departed in his 'silent rocket'. Rex gives chase in his own ship, following his attacker's supersonic beam. He tracks the attacker to Satellite X, where the man, Wolff, opens fire from a revolving control tower. Rex eludes the rays but local monstrosities, aroused by the decimation of their kin, attack the tower, and Wolff is borne away by a winged dragon. Rex rescues Wolff with ray-gun and rope-ladder and, 'securely bound, the space-crook is borne Earthwards to answer for his crimes'. In his second adventure, 'Rex Strong on the Planet Orbona', the Space Ace is sent to report on the inhabitants of a newly discovered planet. He eludes the swarm of flying saucers which greet him with some animosity, and lands in a desolate area. *Zip!* A flexible steel tentacle grabs him and he is taken before Vendit the Dictator. Condemned to fight in an arena with two doors, he is told to choose which to open. One conceals a monster. Mistrusting Vendit, Rex throws both doors open and a monster charges from each! Whilst they fight each other, Rex escapes and is soon heading for Earth, his mission completed.

Nat Brand's last sci-fi hero once again paid tribute to Alex Raymond's famous creation, 'Flash Gordon', echoing in concentrate the original Flash adventure from the mid-Thirties. Brand also illustrated a number of stories for Collins and Children's Press annuals at this time, including one of the colour plates in *Space Story Omnibus*.

THE WORLD OF SPACE

by Ron Embleton
P.R. Publications (1955)

'The first inventors who worked on wonders in the early days were laughed at by others. It was said there could be no such things as gas, electricity, motor-cars and aeroplanes, but they all happened! In just the same way most people will laugh at the idea of interplanetary travel and solar exploration. "Rocket Ships? Travel to the Moon? War with Mars? Battles in Space? Impossible!" they will say. But they most probably will be wrong. This book brings to you some of the wonders of today which may be truth tomorrow!' The sort of introduction that sent thrills down young spines as readers felt themselves drawn into some secret conspiracy against their staid-minded elders. This extremely handsome twenty-four-page book combined strips and stories plus six pages of full colour paintings, all brilliantly executed by the excellent Ron Embleton. The strip, 'The Green Moon', ran across the bottom of each page, telling the adventures of Nick Ballard, ace pilot of Spaceway Freight Services, and his chum, Rock Murphy, pulled off their beam to Planet Jakar and forced down on an unknown moon. Here Sajek, last of the Green Moon Men, and his robots, struggle against Mardo the space pirate. Fortunately Space Hostess Janice turns up to save the chaps, leaving Nick to wonder 'what other terrible adventures await us out there in space?' We shall never know – there was no further edition of *The World of Space*.

Embleton, who signed himself simply 'Ron', also illustrated the text stories, which included 'The Battle of the Space Men', 'Adventure on Mars', 'In the Shadow of the Moon', 'The Monster from the Flying Saucer' and a super-hero story, 'Electron the Great'. This extremely attractive book also had a panoramic cover, the front-page scene carrying over on to the back.

THE MONSTER FROM THE FLYING SAUCER

THE WORLD OF SPACE